101 TALES OF WISDOM

as told by Yogiji Maharaj

Translated by
Sadhu Brahmaviharidas

Swaminarayan Aksharpith
Shahibaug Road, Amdavad
India

101 Tales of Wisdom

Translated by: Sadhu Brahmaviharidas

Inspirer: HDH Pramukh Swami Maharaj

Previous Editions: 1994, 1996, 2000, 2005
4th Edition 1st Reprint: March 2008
Copies: 7,000 (Total: 27,000)
Cost: Rs. 100/-
ISBN: 81-7526-272-9

Published & Printed by
Swaminarayan Aksharpith
Shahibaug, Amdavad-4, India

Websites: www.swaminarayan.org
www.akshardham.com
www.mandir.org
kids.swaminarayan.org

TALES

PREFACE

Of the oldest works of man, fairy tales and other folktales are probably the most loved. The most ancient of stories that we hear narrated around the world, researchers say, originated in Asia, in particular India. Throughout the world people added and omitted, changed and adapted the tales to their own life, local customs and culture.

Folktales originating in India have many distinctive messages — moral and spiritual in nature. Refined over the millennia, the stories have acquired a conciseness and rapidity of narration which are among their principal charms. Yogiji Maharaj's folktales are not to be excluded from this class of stories.

His folktales appeal to the young and old alike. The tales were of all kinds: myths, legends, sagas, fables, comic stories, allegories. Some find their origin in India's vast literary heritage. Others are from the annals of the Swaminarayan Sampraday. Still other stories he seems to have picked from the hustle and bustle of life around him, or at times he has spontaneously created tales from the bubbling childlike innocence that hallmarked his life.

His stories take place in a world inhabited by ordinary people, as well as by all manner of extraordinary characters: giants and dwarfs, cowards and heroes, evil doers and sages. In the midst of everyday affairs wonderful things happen; animals talk, people are transformed into dogs and dragons and back again. In this world, virtue is always rewarded and evil is punished. Worship of God is taught. The help of a true Sadhu is advised.

Invariably, while translating any language, some of the original charm and flavour is lost. Every effort has been made in this book to ensure that 101 Tales of Wisdom transmits the style, impact and enchantment of Yogiji Maharaj. All told, 101 Tales of Wisdom remains delightful and pleasing. This book is a rich storehouse containing many of the well-known and best loved stories. Messages cover a wide range of daily living. The stories are good to read and good to read aloud. Listening to them or reading them, children and adults will all experience some of the enduring wisdom of Yogiji Maharaj.

Tales told by Yogiji Maharaj have already gained widespread popularity. Children eagerly listen to them at bedtime and watch some adapted versions on video! Side by side sit enchanted parents who also read the collected works and narrate them during daily family spiritual time.

The book has been enlivened by excellent semi-symbolic sketches by C.N. Kansara of Amdavad. Inspired by His Holiness Pramukh Swami Maharaj, the direct spiritual successor of Yogiji Maharaj, Pujya Brahmavihari Swami is to be thanked for undertaking the translation work and producing a thoroughly enjoyable 101 Tales of Wisdom.

- Swaminarayan Aksharpith

INTRODUCTION

To unravel ideas through stories is not simply a Hindu tradition but a human tradition. Every great leader has excelled in it. The Zen masters answered intricate questions and paradoxes through anecdotes. Jesus Christ spoke in parables. Ramakrishna Paramahansa profusely narrated stories. Bhagwan Swaminarayan simplified esoteric philosophy through day-to-day illustrations. The sermons of Gunatitanand Swami are alive with stories and examples. And in this same galaxy shines the name of Yogiji Maharaj, one of the loftiest spiritual masters of this century.

His 79 years of presence on this earth, from 1892 to 1971, has left indelible impressions on the spiritual canvas of the world. Apart from his sublime life and experiences, his talks and revelations still resonate in the air. He spoke in the village patois, simple and straightforward. He never lectured, but talked. Even if it was to a packed assembly of 50,000 people, he spoke as if he were talking with individuals with total attention and care.

There was never a question of dressing up ideas in flowery language or veneering the truth with verbal cosmetics. Yogiji Maharaj spoke in plain words and presented the truths in their original, unadulterated, fresh form. When he spoke, his style was naturally picturesque and his gestures were grand, painting the stories in innocent language and visuals. The audiences listened and laughed, thought and wondered, but most of all they understood and grasped. Even if the same spiritual story came from his mouth a hundred times, people hung on to every word, every idea. Such was the magic of his talks.

In all, Yogiji Maharaj had at one time or another, during his talks, narrated more than 2,500 different stories. The learned sadhus who accompanied him noted them down. Of them, Pujya Viveksagar Swami kept the most detailed diary. He noted every word and gesture, writing and rewriting the stories word for word every time Yogiji Maharaj repeated them. From 1958 to 1970, a span of 12 years, Pujya Viveksagar Swami penned more than 25,000 pages of work. With great insight and efficiency, taking care not to prune or cut, alter or touch the original language and style of the great master, he took up the challenge of selecting pearls from an ocean of wealth. His devotion and dedication, coupled with his love for academics and authenticity has resulted in two books, in Gujarati, containing 469 value tales of Yogiji Maharaj. From them, 101 have been translated here. So long as Yogiji Maharaj's tales of wisdom are among us, spiritual truths shall never be too difficult to grasp by people of all nations, of all ages, and of all aspirations.

HOLY TREASURE HUNT

There was a millionaire with a very large business. Unfortunately, his sons were not competent and their poor management brought great damage to the business. Seeing greater loss and damage in the future, the father secretly hid a large sum of his personal wealth. But before passing away, he noted the hiding place in his family book.

In the course of time, all his four sons squandered their money away. Penniless, they started searching for other sources of family wealth. They frantically scoured the family book to find clues to where their father might have buried the extra wealth. And duly, their efforts were rewarded. There in the book was written "At 10 o'clock in the morning, on the tenth day of the bright half of the month of Aso, gold coins have been buried in the mandir pinnacle." The clue seemed loud and clear. Next door to their house was a small Shiv mandir with one pinnacle. Straightaway, they hired a few labourers and broke down the mandir pinnacle. It was a thoughtless thing to do, as they later discovered. All they gathered in their hands was rubble and debris — there were no bags or chests or anything! No treasure at all! Either the book lied or their father lied. Nothing was found from the pinnacle.

However, their desperate need for money compelled them to take the book to a wise man to study the clue. "Fools," he laughed, "you have fooled yourselves. Only I understand the clue in its true sense. Just come along to my house. I'll lend you 500 rupees and with that, go home and reconstruct the pinnacle as it was. Then on the tenth day of the bright half of the month of Aso call me. And when the day arrives, I will show you where the treasure is, not now."

With equal vigour and urgency, the sons restored the pinnacle that they had demolished. Then they waited, restlessly. The day arrived. In the morning at nine o'clock they sent for the wise man. When he reached the mandir pinnacle, the sons said, "Come now, tell us where the money is buried. If it is not in the spire, where is it? Show us our treasure."

"Let us wait till ten o'clock," the wise man calmly responded.

When the time came, the wise man followed the long shadow of the spire on the ground and pointed at its peak, "Dig here."

They marked that place and dug down two arms deep. And to their joy and rejoicement there were 20,000 gold coins sparkling before their eyes.

We clearly see, that when the sons interpreted the clue in their own way, they demolished the mandir pinnacle and were hopelessly misled. But when they found a wise man he led them to the discovery of the treasure and happiness thereafter.

We must beware of this while reading the scriptures. If we draw out our own interpretation from the holy words of God, then it is as damaging as the sons' destruction of the spire. On the other hand, if we approach the true Sadhu and understand the scriptures through him then the 20,000 gold coins will surely be ours. In everything we learn we need an experienced teacher, and if we strive to gain knowledge through our own efforts alone, we are guaranteed to fall.

A TAPASVI'S DETERMINATION

Many people in India perform austerities to please God. A *tapasvi* was performing austerities under a tamarind *(ambli)* tree to please God. He thought if he could please God then he would earn His *darshan*. The *tapasvi* lived on leaves and all day devoutly circumambulated the tree. Because of this continuous ritual of walking around the tree there was a furrow a hand deep.

One day Naradji was going to Vaikunth. He saw the *tapasvi* and approached him. The *tapasvi* bowed down to him and said, "Naradji, as you are going to Vaikunth, ask the Lord on my behalf when He will grant *darshan* to me, as I've been performing austerities for many years, eating only leaves."

Naradji went to Vaikunth and by and by asked the Lord. "A *tapasvi* is performing austerities under a tamarind tree for you to grace him with your *darshan*. When will you grace him? The Lord said, "Tell him that for my *darshan* he will still have to perform austerities for as many years as there are leaves on the tamarind tree!"

Who wouldn't give up on hearing this? Naradji felt weak in the legs. He felt defeated! He thought, "What shall I say to the *tapasvi*. He is sure to lose determination." Naradji left Vaikunth and was making his way back across the sky. The *tapasvi* saw him and so called him. Hearing that Naradji had met the Lord the *tapasvi* was overjoyed. So he asked, "What is God's message for me?"

Naradji replied sadly, "I cannot tell you what the Lord has said. And if I do tell you, you will lose courage and give up your austerities."

The *tapasvi* replied, "No matter what the Lord has said, at least I'll hear His divine words. So tell me, what did He say." Even then Naradji was doubtful. "Shall I tell him," he wondered.

The *tapasvi* again urged him, "Please tell me."

So Naradji said, "The Lord said that even though you have performed austerities for many years, you will still have to perform austerities for as many years as there are leaves on the tamarind tree. Only then will He grace you with *darshan*."

The *tapasvi* was overjoyed! He began to sing and dance, "How lucky I am. God has sent me a divine message! Now it is certain that in the future God will grace me with His *darshan*. The extra years will pass in no time!"

Seeing the *tapasvi's* love and courage, the Lord instantly appeared before him wearing a peacock crown and blessed him. The *tapasvi's* happiness knew no bounds. He was in ecstacy.

Naradji asked God, "Lord! You told me that you would grace him with *darshan* only after he had performed many more years of austerities."

The Lord explained, "Look at his devotion and determination! He didn't lose courage despite the many extra years! To such a person I have to give *darshan*."

If the *tapasvi* had lost faith he would have lost hope. Then would he have had the Lord's *darshan*? Of course not! Never! Always have faith in the words of the great. A determined person reaches his goals early.

In daily life, and for salvation, courage is required, then only does God help us.

THE KING DIES BY SHULI

King Gandu ruled over the city of Andheri, the city of Darkness. Once, a guru and his disciple were roaming in the city. The disciple, somehow, committed a small offence. The king had him caught and sentenced him to death by *shuli* – a method of execution where the victim is laid flat on wooden boards and on top of a sharp iron stake that gradually pierces his body.

King Gandu had given his orders and there was no escaping them. Suddenly, the guru and disciple broke into an argument. The guru said, "Let me go to the *shuli*." And the disciple insisted, "No guruji! No. Give me a chance. Let me go to the *shuli*."

Overhearing their quarrel, the king began wondering, "Why on earth are they competing to die by *shuli*?" He asked them the reason. The guru used a trick. He faked the reason, "The throne of heaven is empty. And at this minute, anyone who dies by *shuli* will attain that throne." The king thought it over and fell for it. "Then why don't I myself die by the *shuli*," he reasoned.

With this thought and his mind dreaming about the kingship of heaven, he climbed to his death.

Both the guru and his disciple were saved because they were united. There was no malice, hatred or disharmony between them. They shared the loving bonds of brotherhood.

JUST GETTING UP!

There was once a *sheth*. In his house he had a chest full of ornaments. One night, thieves broke into his house. His wife, the *shethani,* awoke. The thieves opened the chest!

The *shethani* said to the *sheth,* "Wake up! Thieves have opened the ornament chest!"

The *sheth* said drowsily with his eyes closed, "Just getting up."

The *shethani* said again, "Wake up, they're taking the ornaments!"

The *sheth* yawned, "Just getting up."

The *shethani* screamed, "They've taken everything and are leaving!"

Even then the *sheth* muttered, "Just getting up."

Of what use is this, "Just getting up?"

God and His true Sadhu are shouting warnings. If we awake, salvation is ours. Or else it will be snatched away from us.

AVERAGE KNEE DEEP!

There was a group of fools. They all lived together and trusted each other at all times. It so happened that one day, while journeying to a distant place, they came to a river. They had to cross the river, but none of them knew how to swim. So they stopped by the river bank and put their brains to work. Funnily, the same idea occurred to the whole group.

They thought, "Here, near the river's edge the water is very shallow. Then as one walks into the river it becomes knee-deep. Midway it must be very deep indeed, flowing right above our heads, and then it decreases again as one approaches the other side." So thinking they concluded, "This means the average level of the water is only knee-deep!"

They held hands and happily walked into the river. And, of course, all of them drowned.

One cannot calculate averages while crossing a river. Similarly, one should not apply the law of averages in the spiritual path. It would be foolish to say, "For four days I'll be noble in the company of the enlightened Sadhu, two days I'll be myself and one day I'll enjoy the world with bad company. This should still make me fairly good in the law of averages." One must be fully aware of pitfalls and avoid them at all times.

TAKE A NEEDLE TO HEAVEN

There lived a wealthy *sheth,* but he was a scrooge, mean and miserly. He never spent a rupee, never donated a paisa, and always wore worn shoes and tattered clothes. One day, he fell seriously ill and became bedridden. During his whole life, it was said, he had only one friend, his personal tailor. But unfortunately, he had died a few months earlier. Everyone knew the *sheth's* days were numbered. One by one his family and neighbours came to pay their formal respects. When the tailor's son arrived, the *sheth* said, "It seems that I will not last long here. My moment to rise to heaven has come."

The young boy, though only 15-years-old, was very wise. He knew of the *sheth's* craving for wealth and miserliness. He replied, "O *Sheth,* my father is already in heaven. He often told me that he wished to sew rich garments for the Lord. But he forgot to take his needle with him. Will you please take this needle with you and give it to him."

"Oh, alright, I'll be happy to do that," he agreed.

The *sheth* was happy to do anything as long as it did not involve any giving. He took the needle and gave the boy permission to leave. Alone, in his bed, he began wondering "Where shall I place the needle? Pin it to my shirt? No, that won't do. All my clothes will burn away in my funeral fire. In my mouth. Yes, I'll place the needle in the bulge of my cheek." Then again, he had second thoughts, "But my whole body will be burnt to ashes. How am I to carry this small needle to heaven?" The more he thought about it the more confused he became. Finally, he called the tailor's boy and said, "Son, here, take your needle back. I won't be able to take it to heaven."

"But," the boy looked amused, "if you are going to carry all your millions of rupees to heaven, then why can't you carry one little needle?"

The *sheth's* inner eyes were opened. He realised that none of his wealth or property would accompany him after death. He prayed to God to forgive him for all his past wickedness and promised to profusely donate his wealth in charity should he survive the illness. God cured him and he kept his word. He built a grand mandir, fed thousands and comforted the less fortunate people.

Remember that only wealth which is spent in the service of God, His holy Sadhu and the needy is worthwhile. Our good deeds alone accompany us after death and nothing else will join us.

UNITED WE WIN

A sparrow once laid her eggs on the seashore. Soon the eggs hatched. But a very high tide carried the babies into the sea. The mother sparrow cried all day long.

Then all the sparrows gathered together and decided, "Let's fill in the sea with sand and rescue the babies. Millions of sparrows came together. Each one would dip its beak in the sea and fill it with seawater and then throw it onto the shore. Then every sparrow would pick up a grain of sand or a small pebble and throw it into the sea.

Naradji happened to pass by that way. He saw the millions of sparrows and so asked, "What are all of you doing?"

The sparrows said, "The sea has taken away our babies and so we're filling the sea in." Naradji was astonished at their efforts and faith. He at once went to Vaikunth.

The Lord asked Naradji what the latest happenings on earth were. Garudji was sitting next to the Lord. Naradji answered the Lord in a loud voice so Garudji could hear, "The human race is getting along well, but there is trouble among the birds."

Garudji heard this and asked, "Naradji, why speak ill of my race? What has happened among my people?"

Naradji explained, "Millions of sparrows have united and are trying to save the babies of one sparrow by filling in the ocean. They're working tremendously hard. You yourself belong to the bird race. You should join their efforts. Your not helping them is the trouble and disunity I'm talking about!"

Garudji at once went to the seashore. He filled one of his wings with sand and pushed it into the sea. With each push he filled forty *gau* of sea.

The sea become worried, "Garudji will completely fill me in no time!" he thought to himself. He took a human form and came before Garudji and folded his hands in humility. Garudji said, "Give the babies back." The sea at once gave the babies back.

It was because the sparrows were united that Garudji joined their efforts, and the sea was humbled.

The sea that Garudji filled in is today known as the Bhal region of Gujarat. The water there is salty even today!

If we have unity amongst ourselves God is sure to join our efforts.

NOT A SERVANT OF AUBERGINES

Once there lived a king. He had a very intelligent minister in his royal court. One day someone brought some aubergines as a gift.

The king began complaining, "These brinjals are useless. They're black and fibrous and are not a healthy vegetable to eat."

"Yes, my lord. Yes, you're perfectly correct," supported the minister.

The next day, the king summoned the minister and praised, "Minister, there can be no vegetable better than aubergines. Nothing is tastier or healthier."

"Oh, yes, my lord. These aubergines are the best," the minister continued.

Hearing this, the king questioned, "Minister, why this sudden change? Yesterday, when I deplored the aubergines you shared my opinion by agreeing, and today when I praise them you praise them as well!"

The minister folded his hands and said, "O king, I am not a servant of the aubergines. I am your servant. Whatever pleases you, pleases me. Whatever displeases you, displeases me. I say yes to your yes and no to your no."

The king was pleased by his loyalty and raised his wages by rupees five hundred.

We, too, must say yes to everything said or done by our Guru. This is the stamp of our true service towards him.

GIVING LIFE TO THE DEAD

Four brahmin brothers lived together. Their guru taught them the secret knowledge of Sanjeevani – giving life to the dead. Within two years they had mastered the art and could virtually breathe life into anything they saw!

It was then time for them to return home. During their journey back they found some bones under a tamarind tree. The youngest brother questioned, "Whose bones are these?" The second brother answered, "They look like lion bones."

"Oh let us try out our Sanjeevani knowledge that Guruji has taught us," the youngest said. Not waiting for approval, he mumbled a mantra and sprinkled some water on the bones.

The bones lying here and there rearranged themselves into a skeleton of a lion. The eldest intervened, "These belong to a lion, so avoid the temptation and let us be gone."

The third brother warned, "It's not worth the danger."

Unfortunately, the youngest could not resist the temptation. He chanted a second spell and the bones were covered with flesh and skin. But the lion was still dead. Seeing this the other brothers climbed the tree and pleaded, "Brother, please leave it at this. The lion will kill us all."

Yet the third mantra was said and the lion roared alive. And before its reviver, the youngest brother, could congratulate himself for his amazing feat, the lion sprang and killed him and dragged him into the forest.

This is just a story, but its message is that the other three brothers were also proficient in the knowledge of giving life, but they were wise enough not to use it over a lion. The youngest was foolish and used his knowledge indiscriminately and invited his own death. If he had revived a dead man, at least the man would have been grateful for his entire life and served him well. Therefore, we must always be careful how and where we use our knowledge. Whatever we learn from our guru should always be put to use for good purposes.

DEATH SENTENCE REDUCED TO A THORN PRICK

Many robbers lived in a particular town. Gangs stalked the streets and stole as they willed. Out of these, one particular thief used to regularly attend the spiritual discourses given by the local sadhu. Once, while on his way to the assembly his foot was pricked by a thorn. It became red and swollen. That night he could not join his team for their nightly looting. His friends, however, carried on without him. They broke into the king's treasury and succeeded in escaping with a lot of money. Overnight, they shared the wealth among themselves and slept as millionaires.

Hearing of this success, the family of the thief, scolded him, "Just because you went to the assembly you were hurt, and so failed to join your friends in the robbery. You had to sit here and waste your time and didn't get a single penny!" While these words were being repeatedly said, the king's army arrived. They had tracked the robbers down and collected all of them for execution. Even the innocent thief was lined up for death. But identifying him, the sadhu and the local villagers stood up as witnesses and said that the thief had been hurt by a thorn and so had not gone out stealing that night.

The king pardoned him.

See the rewards of Satsang. Even if we simply sit in the spiritual assembly God protects us. The sentence of death was reduced to the prick of a thorn. These are the words of Bhagwan Swaminarayan in the Vachanamrut and they are the truth.

TRUE FRIENDSHIP

A prince and the minister's son were out hunting in the forests. Both were hungry and exhausted after a long day's wandering. They found the cool shade of a tree and sat down to rest. Soon, the prince fell asleep, while the minister's son stayed awake and kept guard.

A while later a snake slithered towards the prince. Hissing furiously, it prepared to bite him. However, the minister's son was quick. He raised his sword. But before he could kill it, the snake spoke up, "This prince was my enemy in my past life. I cannot rest until I drink blood from his neck."

The minister's son wanted to save his friend's life and he was also intelligent. "Then, what if I give you some of his blood to drink. Will that quench your hate?" Saying this, he knew he was saving the life of the prince because if the snake bit him, to draw blood, it would at the same time spit poison that was sure to kill his friend.

The snake agreed. He was only after the prince's blood, not his life.

The minister's son made a cup out of dry leaves. He climbed upon the chest of the prince who was still fast asleep. He pulled out his dagger and made a small slit on the side of his neck. The sharp cut suddenly shocked the prince awake. But on seeing that his friend, the minister's son, was holding a dagger, he closed his eyes again. The minister's son filled the cup with enough blood and offered it to the snake, which drank the blood and left. Then, the minister's son collected some medicinal herbs and bandaged the wound. A few hours later, the prince awoke and made preparations to proceed further. He said nothing and walked happily as if nothing had happened. Two whole days passed in the forests, yet the prince never reminded him of the event. It was the minister's son who grew impatient as to why he was not questioned.

He finally said, "Friend and master, you know that I climbed upon you and slit your throat, drew blood and then bandaged you. You even saw me do it. Still why haven't you yet questioned me or asked me for an explanation?"

"You are a friend of mine," the prince answered. "I believe that whatever you did must have been for my good. That is why I desire no explanation." He continued, "If someone else had attempted this, I would have been suspicious. Does he want to kill me or rob me? But with you, I know you're a very close friend and I have boundless trust in you — that my friend shall never ever do any harm to me."

This is the mark of true friendship. A friend is he who is harsh to you if it brings greater good. And in return, he who does not sulk or feel hurt by the actions of his friend is a true friend. One should cultivate such intimate friendship with the true Sadhu.

BLACK HANSA IN KALI-YUG

Once upon a time there was a king. One day he commanded his minister, "I want several *hansas* as pets." The minister said, "Sire, only in Satya-yug are white *hansas* to be found. In Treta-yug they are green, in Dwapar-yug, yellow and in Kali-yug, black." The king replied, "That may be so, but I really do want some pet *hansas*."

The minister replied, "In Satya-yug the *hansas* used to graze on pearls. Now they eat *khir* and *puri*."

The king said, "Very good. Find the *hansas*." The minister was a very devious and clever man. He brought twenty black birds from Bhal and put them into a cage. He thought to himself, "Where would I go to find real *hansas*. These will do in their place. The king will never know the truth." He locked them in a cage and everyday would feed them milk, *puri*, *shak* and *khir*.

For six months the deception continued. The holy Sharad Purnima day came. And with it arrived real *hansas*! They settled down in the royal garden.

The crows recognised the true *hansas* and said to themselves, "Our enemies are here. If we have them killed we'll be saved, or else our daily bread will be taken away from us." They were very worried.

The crows went to a guard and said, "Our enemies have come. Only if you shoot them will we stay here."

THE CAMEL'S NECK

A camel performed great austerities. God was pleased and said to it, "Ask whatever boon you desire and it shall be granted."

The camel asked, "Lord, make my neck 400 *gau* long, so that by sitting here I can graze that far away."

"So it shall be," God said. And instantly the camel's neck was 400 *gau* long!

The wild animals of the jungle, tigers, mongooses, foxes all saw the massive neck. They stuck their teeth into its very middle and cut it in half and ate it. The camel died very miserably.

One should perform worldly activities according to one's strength and abilities. By increasing such activities without the ability to cope one will end up like the camel's neck – cut and eaten. Do what little you need to and spend the rest of your time in the worship of God.

COW OR TIGER?

There was a patel. His father died. It is tradition in India that after the death of one's father one should give alms. This is called *punyadan*. So the Patel called a Brahmin and gifted him a cow. The horns and hoofs were decorated with gold. And the cow's back was covered with a beautiful cloak. The Brahmin accepted the cow and started on his way home.

Along the road four thieves saw the Brahmin and the cow. They decided to steal the cow and so made a secret plan. One thief approached the Brahmin and said, "Hey, Bhudev! Where are you taking this tiger? Has that Patel gifted you a tiger because of his father's death?" The Brahmin replied, "What are you talking about! This is a cow!"

The Brahmin walked on. He was soon met by the second thief who said, "Sir, where are you taking this tiger?" A doubt now crept into the Brahmin's mind, "What if it really is a tiger?" He glanced behind to make sure the gift really was a cow.

He walked on through the jungle. Soon the third thief met him and said, "Sir, you are a Brahmin, and you've grabbed this tiger!" On hearing this the Brahmin's doubts grew even stronger. He began to walk at a distance from the cow. He was scared to look behind now. On the road ahead he met the fourth thief who said, "Sir, where did you get this tiger from! It will tear someone up and eat them!"

Now four people had said the same thing to the Brahmin. He was convinced that the cow was a tiger. He ran for his very life, leaving the cow behind. The thieves then took the cow.

If someone tells us, "That person was saying nasty things about you," we readily believe him.

Remember that words are but empty space. If someone calls us *param ekantik* – does it mean that we really are *param ekantik*? If someone calls us a donkey, do we become like a donkey? One should see and hear with correct judgement.

THE SHREW

There was once a shrew. She would never do what her husband asked, but always did the opposite! If told to prepare his bed she would turn the cot upside down. If he asked for water she would offer him a stone! The man was fed up with his wife. He wondered when he'd become free of her.

One day both were crossing a river. The river was in flood and so the shrew held onto the buffalo's tail. Her husband wanted her to be carried away. So he said, "Hold onto the tail tightly." This lady, who always did the opposite of what she was told, at once let go of the buffalo's tail. "There, I've let go!" she exclaimed. The flood waters pulled her away and she drowned.

This is the fruit of such behaviour. God is never pleased if we don't do what we've been told to do. Shriji Maharaj would never allow such a disobedient person near Him.

SHIV, PARVATI AND THE BULL

Once Lord Shiv and his consort, Parvati, were travelling with their vehicle – the Bull. The Lord had taken the form of an old man, while, Parvatiji remained young and beautiful. On the road all passers-by looked on with amazement at this odd couple of an old man and a young woman.

On the way, Shivji said, "Parvatiji, my dear, please sit and ride on the bull during this journey." She obeyed and mounted the bull while Shivji walked alongside. The village folk and other strangers bitterly criticised, "What a selfish woman! She is young and healthy and yet she chooses to comfortably ride while forcing the old man to walk."

So, Shivji changed his mind. "Parvatiji, the people are mocking you. It is wiser that I sit and you walk." So saying, Shivji sat on the bull. Further along, other strangers came with sharper comments, "O look at this mean, bully of a man. He's fat and robust, and evil too. He enjoys the ride while forcing this young and gentle lady to walk on foot."

Hearing this both of them climbed the bull. At least, this would ward off the criticisms. But they were gravely mistaken and no sooner had they come to the next village, people sneered and jeered. "Look at this nasty couple. Both of them have mercilessly climbed upon the bull. They'll kill the poor creature!"

Now there was only one option left. They dismounted and allowed the bull to walk freely. They accompanied it on either side. While they walked, they met new people with new bitterness. They laughed at them, shouting, "What foolishness! They have taken a bull as a vehicle and neither of them are using it."

Straight away Shivji told Parvati, "Come let us do what we think is right, and live the way we want to. The world will never appreciate or see what we do as correct."

In this world, even if we perform a good deed not everyone will like it and support it. The problem lies with the nature of our world. If God's holy Sadhu shows miracles people say, "He's into black magic and possesses evil powers." And if the Sadhu avoids miracles, some will mutter complaints, "O! He shows no miracles. He's ordinary and is of no use." This is the line of thinking our world works on. It is crooked from both ends and whatever you do, the world will never see you straight. Therefore, pay no attention to the words of the worldly people and continue to devoutly worship God.

"DON'T LOOK!"

Not so long ago there lived a carpenter. Everyday he went to work at the home of a Portuguese ruler in Div. The mistress of the house was very beautiful.

While he worked on his wood, the carpenter saw the master and his wife seated in the balcony. He could not control himself and started throwing glances at the lady. The master noticed this and warned the carpenter, "Don't look!" But the poor man's mind had been deeply drawn by her looks. He continued to steal glances and the master threatened him three times, "Don't look!"

On the fourth occasion, the master became so enraged that he took a chisel and blinded the carpenter by gouging his eyes out.

Did the carpenter gain anything by staring at the lady? He suffered great misery because he was unable to control his mind. If one has attained the Gunatit state (enlightened state) then one is not tempted by anything.

THE LETTER WILL SPEAK

There was a rich merchant. He once had to send twenty sticks of sugarcane to a man in another village. To take the sugarcane he called an illiterate worker. The merchant wrote a short letter concerning the sugarcane. Giving the letter to the worker he said, "Take this sugarcane to so and so village. I will pay you one rupee." The worker asked, "How many sticks are there?" The merchant replied, "Give this letter to the man who receives the sugarcane, and the letter will speak for itself."

The worker picked up the sugarcane and letter and started off. He had walked some fifteen kilometres when he developed a desire to eat some sugarcane. The silly man asked the letter, "How many sticks of sugarcane are there?" Would the letter reply? The man began to beat the letter. But even then it didn't say anything! In the end he became irritated and ate two sticks anyway.

He carried the remaining eighteen sticks to the village and gave them with the letter to the man. The man read the letter and counted the sticks. There were two less. He asked the worker, "In the letter it is written twenty sticks, and yet you have given me only eighteen?"

"Sir, who told you?" the worker asked surprised. "The letter spoke to you but why didn't it speak to me? I threatened it and hit it. Even then it didn't say a word!"

Only one who is learned can make a letter 'speak'. What can an illiterate do?

In the same way, only a person who has learnt the teachings of the Vachanamrut from a God-realised Sadhu can understand the principles and inner meanings of the scripture.

DURYODHAN AND YUDHISHTHIR

Somebody asked Duryodhan, "In all of God's creation, do you know any-one who has a bad temper?" "Everyone has a bad temper," Duryodhan replied.

A person asked Yudhishthir, "Are there any unrighteous people in the world?"

"Everyone is righteous," Yudhishthir replied.

We are what we see around us.

KUKADDAM

Foxes are very sly animals. There was one very cunning fox. He was craftier than all the rest. He would steal *barfi*, *ghari*, *mesub*, and other sweets from the sweet shop regularly. The shop owner noticed his stock disappear everyday. "I'll have to catch the thief," he thought to himself.

One night the owner sat awake. Two o'clock at night the fox came. The shopkeeper felled him with a chair. He then dragged the fox outside. The fox was still alive. He decided to just lay there and pretend to be dead. The next morning the village got together. They found out that the sweet shopkeeper had killed a fox. It was decided to punish the owner. The fox lay quietly listening to everything. He thought it right that the owner be punished.

After a little while a carpenter came by. He said to the shopkeeper, "I'd like to take away the fox's tail." The owner said, "Take it. Cut it off."

The fox decided, "Let him take my tail. I won't say a word. But I want that shopkeeper punished." The carpenter cut off the fox's tail and went away pleased.

After a little while another man was passing. He said to the shopkeeper, "I'd like the fox's ears." "Cut them and take them," replied the shopkeeper. The man did so. A third man arrived, he said, "I'd like the fox's teeth." Hearing this the fox thought. "If these go I'll really end up dead. How will I eat without teeth?" And so he jumped up and ran for his very life.

And now it so happened that a dyer was making colour in a small pit. The fox jumped into it. When he came out he was coloured red and yellow all over.

No one recognised the strangely coloured fox with no ears and no tail. All the animals were scared of him and would run away on his approach. The fox named himself Kukaddam. He began making plans to become king of the forest.

One day, he proudly declared to those who were frightened of him, "I am king of the forest. You shall all obey me from now onwards." All the wild animals began to come to him and pay homage. For his protection the fox placed sentries in three circles around him. In the inner circle near to him there were only foxes. In the next circle were men and finally the tigers and lions. He ordered them, "You should stand guard six kilometres distant from here."

Two months passed in this way. Winter arrived. The foxes began to howl in the cold. Kukaddam would also quietly howl with those foxes around him. In the colder months they would howl more.

One day, the tiger and lion said to themselves, "We're the original kings of the forest, and so it is not right that we are not allowed to go near the king." They went to Kukaddam with their request, "Sire, we were the previous kings of the forest. For two months the foxes have stayed near Your Highness. Please send them away and let us stay close to you as your personal bodyguards. Kukaddam could not stop himself from saying yes. The tiger and lion stood close to him as guards.

In the cold Kukaddam felt an urge to howl as before. In the distance the other foxes began to howl. But what could he do. If he howled he would be caught and everyone would kill him. The cold soon increased and the desire to howl became even greater. Kukaddam would make strange noises in his throat, "Oohoo, Oohoo," The lion asked him, "Sire, what is wrong? Does your stomach hurt?"

What answer could the fox give. Slowly, the noises increased and then Kukaddam couldn't resist any longer – he began to howl. The lion at once realised, "This Kukaddam is a fox! He's fooling us." With one pounce he killed the pretender.

The truth can never be hidden for long. Even by eating garlic in secret its smell cannot be hidden. In the same way, just by wearing the clothes of a sadhu and declaring oneself to be a great soul one does not become so. Such an impostor is sure to be exposed. One should become a real sadhu. Weakness for the sense pleasures can be compared to Kukaddam's howling.

MILLION TIMES CONVINCED

In a forest lived a rabbit, a snake, a tortoise and a fox. They were all friends. Once, as they sat talking, a question was raised. What would they do if the forest caught fire?

The rabbit said, "I'm a hundred times convinced that I'll hide in my house."

The snake said, "I'm hundred thousand times convinced that I'll climb to the top of a tree."

The tortoise said, "I'm a million times convinced that I'll dig a hole and squeeze into it."

Listening to all these ideas the fox said, "Brothers, I have only one conviction and that is that if the forest really did catch fire I would run out of the forest. If the fire comes from that direction I'll run in this opposite direction. But I won't stay around anywhere in the forest."

And one day it really did happen. The forest caught fire. To escape from the fire the rabbit rushed into his home. The snake climbed a tree. The tortoise dug a hole in the earth and squeezed in. And the fox ran away. The fire spread throughout the forest. All the animals scattered. When the fire finally blew itself out the fox returned to see how his friends had fared.

He looked into the rabbit's borrow and saw that the hundred times convinced rabbit had been boiled. The fox looked up at the tree and saw that the hundred thousand times convinced snake was hanging limp. And the million times convinced tortoise had been baked.

The fox was convinced that it is better to have only one strong but correct conviction!

Similarly we should have only one conviction that "I want to worship God." We should be influenced by only Shriji Maharaj and Swami.

At the cost of even a million tasks we should ensure our salvation.

WHOSE BEARD WILL YOU SAVE FIRST?

Once the king and his attendant, Lava, were relaxing. The king asked, "Tell me, Lava, how much love do you have for me?"

"Infinite," replied Lava.

"Then," the king continued, "if my beard and your beard catch fire at the same time, whose will you save first?"

"O beloved king!" Lava replied, "You are the mighty ruler, the great master, yet I would stroke my beard once or twice first to put out the fire and then douse your beard."

Likewise, we should strive for our own salvation first.

HIRO GOES TO GHOGHA

Bhavnagar is a very old city. A simpleton named Hiro lived there. He worked at a Sheth's office. The Sheth called him one night and told him. "Hira, tomorrow morning you'll have to go to Ghogha." Ghogha was a nearby town with a busy port. The Sheth was to give him all the details in the morning, but Hiro never bothered to inquire the reason of his mission, why he was to go to Ghogha, or what he was to do there? The next morning, without meeting his master, he walked 24 miles to Ghogha. Having reached there, and not knowing what to do, he plucked one leaf from a tree and returned to the office.

The Sheth fumed, "Did I sent you there to bring back a leaf?"

Similarly, we have been given birth on this earth. We have built bungalows, earned fame, and done so many other things; but they are all like Hiro going to Ghogha and bringing back a leaf. The true goal of our life should be clear. Why have we come here? We must strive to earn the grace of the holy Sadhu and please God.

HE PLACED HIS HEAD BETWEEN THE COW'S HORNS

In a village there lived a man named Moti Patel. He would awake at six o'clock every morning and brush his teeth with a *datan* stick, while sitting on a stone seat in front of his yard. Every morning at that same time a cow would come and sit there and chew cud.

The cow's horns were nicely rounded and Motibhai would think to himself everyday, "My head would fit snugly between the two horns!" So, he began to promise himself everyday, "I'll fit my head in today or tomorrow." In this way six months passed. Then one day he made up his mind. "I'll definitely fit my head between those beautiful horns today." After he finished cleaning his teeth he stood up and went to the cow. He put his head between the cow's horns. It fit snugly. But the cow jumped up in fright and ran. Motibhai was pulled along.

"Help! Help! Help!" he screamed. The village people caught the cow and pulled Motibhai's head free.

They scolded the battered and bruised Patel. "Motibhai, why didn't you stop to think before doing this?" Motibhai replied, "I did. Only after six months of serious thought did I put my head between those horns!" Motibhai broke his arms and legs. He got better after two long months.

This is just a story. The principle to be understood is that Motibhai thought for six months before fitting his head between the cow's horns. But the thought itself was wrong. To achieve salvation one should think only positive thoughts. And only then will we one day achieve our goal.

PROGRESS WITHOUT PRAISES

There was once a painter. He would paint *murtis* of God. His son would also paint beautiful *murtis* of the Lord. After completing each *murti* the son would show it to his father. But his father would always find fault with it, "Not very good. It needs improvement." The next day the boy would show the improved painting to his father. But his father would say, "The eyes are incorrect. Improve them." Sometimes he would say, "The head needs correction."

Once, the son said to himself. "My father will never say my paintings are good." So one day he painted a beautiful *murti* of the Lord and buried it in the ground. After a month he dug it up and said, "Father, I've found this *murti* hidden in the ground." He showed the *murti* and asked, "Father, what do you think of this *murti*?" His father praised, "Very good. You should paint like this." His son said at once, "But father, I've painted this *murti*!"

His father was saddened, "From now on you will never improve. I used to scold you about your paintings so you would always try to do better. Your brush won't improve beyond this point now," he explained.

The enlightened Sadhu scolds us only to carry us forward. Therefore, only think of his virtues. Never feel badly towards him.

TUKARAM

Tukaram was a great saint of Maharashtra. He was always singing *bhajans*. Once, on the festival of Hutashini, some kids came to Tukaram. They, being mischievous, said, "Sing some *fag*." Tukaram refused. So the children grabbed hold of Tukaram and shaved off all the hair from his head. They then painted his head white with lime. As if this was not enough they sat him backwards on a donkey and gave him the donkey's tail to hold! They garlanded him with a garland made of carrots and aubergines. The kids then took him all around the village, shouting and making fun of poor Tukaram all the way.

When Tukaram's wife Janbai saw this, she burst into tears. But Tukaram said to her, "Why are you crying? What wrong has been done? My hair was long and I didn't have the money to cut it, so the kids cut it free of charge! And I also have dandruff but now the lime will cure it. And when we got married did we have a procession? No, so we had it today! Plus the vegetable garland will do as food for a few days."

Tukaram was very humble. Another person would have been greatly insulted. He tolerated everything, and now the whole of Maharashtra sings the praises of Tukaram and Janbai.

GOD'S WILL OR MY SKILL!

A sadhu was passing through one village. He saw a rich crop of wheat in one farmer's field. Pleased and delighted he said, "What a beautiful crop! It's all because of God's grace and will."

"No, no!" the farmer protested, "It has nothing to do with God's will. It's all due to my skill. I'm the one who has ploughed and perspired, not God! It's my back that aches, not God's. This golden crop is the result of my efforts, not God's!"

Not replying, the sadhu walked on. After some time, he happened to pass by the same farm again. This time he was saddened to see that the whole crop was diseased. It was dying. He remarked, "Oh, my! The crop is dying of a disease."

"Yes, what can I do? God has ruined me!" the farmer lamented.

This is the way of our selfish world. When something good happens, man tries to take full credit for it and boasts of his own skill; and when some calamity strikes, man blames it on God's will. We must always be aware of the power of God. It is only His will that guides the whole universe.

THE PROUD CHARAN

Panchal is an ancient part of India. A Charan lived there. He was very proud and held himself in high esteem. Self-praise was his way of life.

One day, he sat gossipping and smoking his pipe in the village square. It so happened that a small spark sprang from the burning pipe and fell on one of the men sitting around him. The man gave out a loud cry of pain and stood up. The Charan laughed and ridiculed such cowardly behaviour on the part of the man.

"But even the bravest of the brave would jump up and run if a burning ember fell on his body," someone said.

"Yes, others may run but not I!" the Charan boasted.

"Then let us see and put you to the test." Some of the villagers took this opportunity to sober him up. But the Charan proudly accepted. He drenched his clothes with oil and resumed his smoking with greater style.

"Come on, set me on fire," he dared the men. One person came forth and lighted him. A sudden blaze roared alive. "Tie him down by the legs so that he doesn't run away," someone suggested.

"Others may run but not I!" said the Charan. And he stood there with the end of his smoking pipe in his mouth while he burnt to death.

A man is ready to even burn himself for the sake of pride. Ego is a silent enemy. It ruins us. So give up ego and approach God and His true Sadhu. By understanding their glory one is freed from ego and self-pride.

JANAK AND THE NINE YOGESHWARS

King Janak lived in the city of Mithila. Once the nine Yogeshwars came there. At once King Janak got off his throne and embraced all the Yogeshwars at the same time. Seeing this, a person thought, "Has the King gone mad? Like a madman he embraced all the Yogeshwars together!"

He asked, "King Janak, why did you embrace them all together?" The King replied, "This, my body, is temporary; it may die any moment. And if it did fall just now I'd have missed the chance to embrace the Yogeshwars. I have not gone mad."

Janak then embraced the Yogeshwars again, but this time one by one.

What perfect awareness King Janak had! It can never be foretold how long the body will live. And so worldly activities should not be given prime importance. Worship God before it is too late!

DAY DREAMER

A day dreamer worked as a freelance servant, looking for odd jobs around the village. One day, a wealthy *sheth* offered to pay him two *annas* to carry ten kilogrammes of ghee to his home. It was only one mile away. The day dreamer eagerly agreed. No sooner had he put the pot of ghee on his head and begun his journey, then his thoughts ran free. He fantasised step by step, "This job will fetch me two *annas*, from which I'll purchase a goat. The goat will give me good milk which will bring more money. Then I'll get myself a fine wife and have children. By that time, I shall have enough money to open a small business. When seated in my shop, my son will come to call me for lunch, but of course, there will be so many customers, and I'll be so busy that I'll have to refuse and say, 'No, not now.' "

And the day dreamer shook his head. As he did so, the pot of ghee dropped to the ground and shattered to pieces. The *sheth*, walking alongside him was furious, "Oh you careless fool, you've broken my pot!"

"For you, only your pot has been broken. For me, my home and all my hopes have been shattered," the day dreamer replied with gloom.

We too revel in grand fantasies of earning huge wealth, building factories, great successes. But all materialistic thoughts are mere daydreams, everything of this world is false and perishable. Our fantasies will shatter one day.

THE CAMEL'S LIP

There was once a fox. One day, he saw the lower, drooping lip of a camel. He thought to himself, "The camel's lip is hanging and it will fall off any time. It must be very soft and tasty. I must eat it."

With this thought he began to run in front of the camel, constantly watching the camel's hanging lip. He ran four kilometres in this way but the lip didn't fall. The fox was disappointed and went away.

A camel's lower lip never falls, despite its drooping. The pleasures of the world are comparable to the camel's lip. Everyone is running here and there to get them. But nothing falls into their hands. Life ends while they're still running.

"I'VE SEEN YOU!"

Four sadhus arrived at a village. In the evening assembly many Hindus had gathered. The sadhus sang *kirtans* very well and so some Muslims also came to listen to them. The sadhus talked to the Muslims. They asked one old Muslim to take a vow. The old man refused, but when the sadhus explained to him he finally agreed. The old Muslim said, "I will keep only one vow. In this village you have a potter devotee. I promise that only after his *darshan* will I eat anything." The sadhus agreed. And so every morning the Muslim would go to the potter's house for his *darshan*, say, "Jai Jai," and then return home.

In this way six weeks passed. One day the potter woke up early and set off with his donkeys to go and dig some clay. When the Muslim arrived at his home he saw that the door was locked. He asked a neighbour, "Where is the potter?" The neighbour answered, "He woke up early and has gone to dig clay in that direction."

The Muslim was hungry. He had not had supper the previous night. He was in a hurry to have the potter's *darshan* and then eat a *rotlo*. So he quickly walked in the direction the potter had gone.

The potter was digging clay and filling sacks hanging from the donkeys' backs. As he dug he struck a pot of treasure! He opened the pot and saw it was filled with rupees! He was overjoyed and decided to hide it in a sack and take it home.

Just then from a distance the Muslim saw the potter. The Muslim had the potter's *darshan* and shouted, "Jai Jai," and began walking home. He was very hungry.

The potter thought the old Muslim had seen the treasure pot and was hurrying away to tell the king. So he shouted, "Brother, wait a minute." The Muslim shouted back, "I've seen you. I've seen you!" The potter was now really shocked. He was convinced the Muslim had seen the potful of rupees and was now going to tell the whole village. And if the king found out he would take everything. The potter ran after the Muslim shouting, "Just a minute! Half of it is yours!"

The Muslim stopped. What was the potter devotee talking about? The potter caught up with the Muslim and explained, "While digging the clay I found a pot filled with two thousand rupees! Half of it is yours. But don't tell anybody. At twelve midnight we will split the booty. The Muslim understood everything at once and readily agreed. He was no longer hungry. They hid the pot in a sack and took it home on the donkey's back.

At midnight the two got together and divided the treasure equally.

The Muslim thought, "I took just one vow because of the sadhus, and look how well I've done. How much more will I gain if I take more vows? Surely I shall be granted salvation." The old Muslim from that day on became a devotee of God.

WISE MEN THINK ALIKE

There lived a very prosperous king. One day, he decided to hold a huge public feast for all his citizens. "The main dish should be *dudhpak*," he thought. To feed everyone he needed 100 *maunds* of milk. Now that's a lot of milk. The king found a simple way of getting it. He called 100 wealthy businessmen and ordered, "I am preparing a special pool in the village square. Tomorrow early morning, I want each one of you to pour one *maund* of milk into the pool. It is my desire to serve *dudhpak* to the entire city."

Everyone agreed. They returned to their homes and gave it serious thought. One businessman reasoned, "I'll start early and in the dark morning hours before dawn, I'll go and pour one *maund* of water. Since there will be ninety-nine *maunds* of milk poured by the other men one *maund* of water should make no difference. It'll pass unnoticed. And nobody will ever see me in the dark!"

It would have been fine if only one of them had had this thought. But, coincidently, each one of them was clever and each one had the same thought!

The next morning, each businessman silently poured his *maund* of water into the pool. When dawn broke, the pool shimmered to the brim with water. The king arrived at the scene and was shocked. He summoned all the businessmen and said, "I had commanded you to fill up this pool with pure milk and there isn't even a drop of milk in this!"

The businessmen looked at each other and chorused, "O king! Wise men think alike."

The king was quick to understand the situation. His anger and annoyance lessened and turned into appreciation. He praised the oneness of their mind and congratulated them for their unity.

We, too, should cultivate such subtle unity with our fellow devotees. We must think alike and never allow differences of opinion or thoughts to divide us. If we remain rooted to the refuge of God and live in harmony with one mind then we shall be able to achieve whatever goal we decide upon.

AMBARISH AND DURVASA

King Ambarish was an *atmanivedi* – an humble servant of God. Both he and his queen were performing great austerities. For twelve months they had fasted on every *ekadashi*, not even drinking water. Their fast would end on Kartik *sud* 12. On the morning of the twelfth, Sage Durvasa and one hundred of his disciples arrived at King Ambarish's palace. Ambarish was overjoyed. He fell at their feet and welcomed them. He said, "Today my *ekadashi* fast ends, and on this day you have also graced my palace. Indeed, I am very fortunate! Please dine here today." Durvasa replied, "We'll first go to the river for a bath and then return."

Durvasa and his disciples went to the river. There is a saying, "Buffaloes, Brahmins and spinnach, have only to see water to be delighted!" And so Durvasa and his disciples bathed for a long time. But the sacred time for ending the fast was approaching. The king's Brahmins advised him, "The *muhurt* is passing. It is best you eat and so end the fast." Ambarish said, "I shall eat when Durvasa returns." The Brahmins replied, "But it is getting late. Only a few moments are left now. If you eat afterwards you will not receive the fruits of your fast." Ambarish was troubled. But Brahmins are very clever. They found an easy answer. They said, "Eat a sanctified tulsi leaf. In this way it can be said you have ended your fast, and yet it can also be said that you haven't eaten a meal!"

On the Brahmins' advice Ambarish placed a tulsi leaf in his mouth. Just then Durvasa and his disciples arrived. They discovered that Ambarish had completed his fast in their absence.

Durvasa never needs to search for anger. It's always with him as his constant companion. He shouted, "Ambarish, you are known as a great devotee, yet you have no idea of how to treat your guests! Why did you eat alone without us!"

Ambarish touched Durvasa's feet in apology. He said, "Only to safeguard the *muhurt* have I placed a leaf of tulsi in my mouth. The banquet is ready. Come, let us dine together."

But would Durvasa listen? No! He was the very incarnation of anger. Cursing Ambarish he cried, "You shall have to suffer the fruits of insulting me." Saying this he plucked a hair from his head and transformed it into a demonness. He commanded her to beat Ambarish.

Now, Ambarish was truly a great devotee of the Lord. He stood with hands joined in humility. The Lord placed his special weapon, the Sudarshan Chakra, in Ambarish's protection. The Sudarshan Chakra began to spin. Its bright light burnt the demonness to ashes. It then moved towards Durvasa to burn him as well. Durvasa saw this. He became frightened and shouting, *"Trahi toba,"* clenched his fists and began to run for his dear life. The Chakra chased him everywhere.

Screaming *"Pahi mam! Pahi mam!* Save me! Save me!" Durvasa went to

Lord Shiv and asked that he be saved from the Sudarshan Chakra. Shiv replied, "I cannot turn the Chakra back. It belongs to Lord Vishnu. Go to him."

For a whole year Durvasa ran. He finally went to Lord Vishnu crying. "*Pahi mam*! *Pahi mam*! Save me! Save me!" he begged, "Lord, I cannot suffer the light from your Sudarshan Chakra anymore. I'm burning. Please call the Chakra off." God said, "Durvasa, once my Chakra has been thrown at a person it never returns without killing him. I have no solution." Durvasa began to weep. God said to him, "No good will be done by weeping. But yes, there is one way of saving yourself."

"Lord! Quick tell me."

"But will you be able to do it?"

"Lord, if my life can be saved anything and everything will be done!" said Durvasa, in an humble voice.

The Lord explained to Durvasa, "You have insulted my devotee, Ambarish. Humbly go to him and fall at his feet. If he forgives you then the Chakra will return to me."

In a time of great need we may even address a donkey as 'father'. To live, Durvasa had no other option. And so after a year of suffering, Durvasa went to Ambarish. From the moment Durvasa had run away, with the Chakra chasing him, King Ambarish had remained standing at the place he had been insulted. He had not eaten or drunk anything.

"*Pahi mam*! *Pahi mam*!" cried Durvasa. He fell at King Ambarish's feet. Ambarish pulled his feet away and raised Durvasa. He said, "King of sages, your falling at my feet is not right." Durvasa replied, "Ambarish, you are a true devotee of the Lord. I have insulted you. Please forgive me. Save me from the Sudarshan Chakra."

King Ambarish prayed to the Sudarshan Chakra and said, "If the love and respect I have for Durvasa at this moment are the same as they were when he first came to my palace, then, O Sudarshan Chakra! Please return to the Lord." The Sudarshan Chakra returned to Lord Vishnu at once.

Durvasa was tremendously relieved. Then both he and Ambarish together went to the banquet hall.

God cannot tolerate an insult thrown upon a great devotee of His. So never take fault with any devotee. Being humble before such a devotee pleases God.

LIFE IS BUT A DREAM

His Majesty, King Janak, the ruler of Mithila, once had a dream. In the dream he was a starving beggar. For seven days he had gone without food. He went to Delhi and begged, "Please, will someone give me a morsel to eat?" He had no money. He asked if there was an almshouse nearby. "Yes, there's one where they give free rice to eat," someone guided him.

He found the almshouse but the man in charge was quick tempered. He ordered, "Bring your own bowl for food." King Janak had nothing with him, and so searched for a potter. After a while, he came to a potter's house but he abused him with foul language and closed his doors. Hopeless and depressed, Janak turned to the garbage heaps, looked through litter and found a broken clay vessel. He got his share of food and moved to a small corner to sit and quietly eat. Just then, two bulls which had run loose, came near him and started a furious duel. Scared, Janak got up, and as he tried to save himself his portion of food fell. He was shocked and paralysed with fear.

Just then his eyes opened. The dream abruptly ended. He shook himself out of his sleep and heard his guards sound the trumpets and call, "Victory to His Majesty, the noble king of the City of Mithila."

He was in his richly ornamented bed in his royal bedroom. He was lost in deep thought, "Which is real? The dream or this kingdom?" He approached his guru, Ashtavakra. "O Guruji, in my dream I could not even eat a morsel, such was my fear; and now I walk supreme as a king, which is real out of the two?"

Ashtavakra replied, "Neither! Even this life is a dream. That was a short dream and this life is perhaps a sixty, seventy or eighty year long dream!"

The things of this world are short-lived, only temporary.

A MOUNTAIN OF VEGETABLES

One *Kachiya* devotee, a greengrocer by profession, came to Mumbai. It was his first visit to this famed city of wealth and luxury. He decided to spend three full days sightseeing. He was asked, "Have you seen the city?"

"Yes," he said.

"What did you see?"

"In the Bhaikhala market I saw great heaps of vegetables. Tons and tons of vegetables. Gosh! My God! A mountain of vegetables!" the devotee replied.

There are a lot of places and things to see in Mumbai. But the greengrocer saw only the vegetables. We all choose to see only what we are interested in. Similarly, he whose mind is attached to God, and delights in God, sees nothing else but God.

A COPPERSMITH'S CAT

There once lived a cat who lived with a copper-smith. The cat had become accustomed to the constant din of a hammer beating pots and pans into shape. One day the cat sneaked into the home of a Patel. She drank all the milk, and ate the yogurt and other food. When the Patel found out he started banging a metal plate to scare the cat away. But this was a copper-smith's cat. Would she be frightened of such a noise! She remained unperturbed.

Likewise, I talk to you but your ears have become accustomed to our teachings. The drums have already been played. So of what use is a mere tinkling.

Do not be like the coppersmith's cat. Strengthen your heart and life by the messages of the discourses you hear.

ALL THINGS COME AND GO

A fakir was walking along a road. He found a rope lying on the road. Thinking that it would be useful in the future he hung it around his shoulder. He walked on. Sometime later, the rope slowly slipped off the shoulder. The Fakir was so engrossed in his walking that he never realised the rope was missing. He neither stopped nor slowed, and continued his journey. It was only after he had travelled a great distance that he realised the absence of the rope. He searched for it, looking over both his shoulders. It wasn't there. "What's the use of going all the way back looking for the rope?" the Fakir reasoned. "I never did find a rope," he thought, and thus wiping away the rope from his mind he happily walked on.

To live happily in this world we all have to train ourselves to take a positive mental attitude. We must educate our minds to accept the system of Sankhya, which teaches that everything except God, His abode and the liberated souls, is perishable. All other things come and go, nothing is permanent.

TODAY AND EVERYDAY

Once apon a time there were two ladies. They both had a brother each. One sister had great love for her brother. She once said to the other lady, "Sister, if my brother leaves today. He'll come back a...ll the way tomorrow."

The other sister didn't love her brother so much.

Her brother would only come to see her once a year. But she said, "My brother comes too often. He's here today and everyday."

This is not a sign of true love.

Even if we associate with a true Sadhu all day long we should feel we have not associated enough. Never be satisfied. Through constant holy association we realise the greatness of God and His Sadhu. It is only the very fortunate who have the chance to serve God and His Sadhu.

IS YOUR FATHER CHEWING FOR ME!

A *sheth* sat down to eat. His wife was fanning him. Even then he was sweating a lot. The *sheth's* wife asked him, "I place the food in your mouth, I fan you as well, I do all the work and yet why do you sweat so?"

The *sheth* replied, irritated, "Is your father chewing for me! I have to chew for myself! That's why I'm sweating."

God has given us this human body. He has given us our intelligence and strength. He has done everything possible. Now it is for us to put in the effort and worship God. Never become irritated in worshipping God.

A QUIVER OF ARROWS

Great kings are great teachers. There was once such a king. His ministers had no unity amongst themselves. To teach them unity the king commanded that a quiver full of arrows be brought to the court. When it arrived he said, "Anyone who can snap this whole quiver into two will be given my kingdom."

All the ministers, one after the other, tried but none could break the quiver.

Then the king took one arrow from the quiver and asked a minister to break it into two. Even the weakest of the weaklings could do this!

The king explained to his ministers, "If you have unity in the same way as these arrows when they are together, then we will be victorious everywhere."

Gunatitanand Swami has said in his sermons, "If all of you – sadhus, *parshads, brahmacharis* and devotees – live with unity, then no matter how strong your inner enemies may be, you will be able to defeat them. But if you have no unity, then even the smallest of faults will drive you out of Satsang.

PATIENCE

In the region of Marwad, a traveller, was spent and exhausted after walking 34 miles in one day. The village he had set out for was now not too far away. But enough was enough. He was tired and had lost all patience. Just then, he saw a stranger coming from the opposite direction. He stopped to inquire, "How far is the village?"

"Oh it is only two miles from here!" the stranger replied.

But the traveller had no patience left to help him. He questioned, "Two miles from where you're standing or from where I'm standing?"

When we lose faith and patience we cannot proceed any further towards the completion of our goal. Therefore, never allow your patience to falter and fade in any work you undertake.

THE LAZY MAN

A lazy man was sleeping under a *rayan* tree. A small *rayan* fell on his chest. However, he was too lazy to put the fruit into his mouth. He waited for someone to pass by. After a while he saw a camel rider in the distance. So he shouted, "Camel rider, please stop!"

The camel rider thought to himself, "The poor man might be ill and may want to drink some water or need other help." So he stopped his camel and walked half a field over to the lazy man. He asked, "What can I do?" Remaining lying down the lazy man said, "A *rayan* has fallen on my chest, kindly put it into my mouth!"

The camel rider became cross. He said, "I got off my camel and walked across half a field to you. And this is the only reason you called me for?" He strode off very angry.

The lazy man called after him, "You're a very lazy fellow! All you had to do was put the *rayan* in my mouth."

The lazy man had only to put the *rayan* into his mouth and yet he called somebody else. How can such a person get ahead in life?

Satsang can be compared to the *rayan* fruit falling on our chest. Shedding laziness, we should take full benefit of Satsang.

JANAK VIDEHI

King Janak was a *videhi*. In his kingdom lived two Brahmin friends. One was a scholar. The scholar one day said, "Come, let's go to King Janak and ask him why he is called 'Videhi'."

"Forget it, one should never meddle with a king, a musician or a monkey. Their minds are never stable. They might do anything to us," said the other Brahmin.

"But what's wrong in asking?" argued the scholar.

After a while both went to King Janak. The palace guards took them to the king immediately.

King Janak welcomed them. "Why have you come?" he asked.

"Why are you called Videhi?" the friends asked. Hearing this the King immediately commanded, "Catch hold of these Brahmins. Tie them up." The Brahmins were frightened. The ignorant Brahmin said, "I told you so. Never trust a king, a musician or a monkey."

The King then said, "Take them to a big house. Look after them well. Tomorrow morning at 10 o'clock they will be hanged."

The ordinary Brahmin was now regretting his coming, "I said we shouldn't have come. This man is a king. His mind is never balanced!"

The house they were taken to was better than a luxurious royal home!

There was everything for the Brahmins. Soft mattresses, mosquito nets, the lot. But all the Brahmins could see was the hanging. They didn't enjoy any of the luxuries. At twelve in the afternoon lunch was brought in on golden plates. There was milk, *puri*, *shak*. But they could eat nothing. All they could see was the hanging.

The home became like a prison. They enjoyed nothing. The delicious food tasted tasteless! The night seemed to last a year. And the Brahmins could only talk of their troubles!

Morning dawned. Hot water for bathing arrived in golden buckets. But all that the Brahmins could see was the hanging.

The scholarly Brahmin had a thought. He called a servant of the king and said to him, "God has given us this human body to worship Him. Now, if we are hanged, we will not gain salvation. So go and request the king to punish us in some other way."

But the servant instead took them both to the king. They explained, "We have not worshipped God, we don't involve ourselves in *satsang* and neither have we accepted a guru. So please change our punishment!"

King Janak commanded at once, "Bring here two large golden bowls. Fill them to the brim with oil. Give them to these Brahmins to hold, and then make them walk throughout Mithila. On both sides have a guard with a sword ready. If even a drop of oil is spilt then chop their heads off!"

The two Brahmins were really depressed now. But they had to obey. There were many things to hear and see in Mithila, but the Brahmins thought only of the oil. They toured Mithila for three hours, concentrating on the oil, lest their heads be chopped off.

Finally they returned to King Janak. He welcomed them, "Come wise Brahmins, tell me, when I first commanded that you be hanged, did you enjoy the golden plates, beds, velvet and all the other luxuries?"

"Sir, even though you sent us food we didn't eat. Our minds were on the hanging. We were scared of the clock striking ten. We didn't enjoy anything. We touched nothing!"

"And what did you see in your three-hour walk in Mithila?"

"We looked only at the golden bowls, and concentrated on the oil. The swords were glinting in the light. We just about made it back to your palace."

"Now, listen to me," said the King. "I have this whole kingdom to care for, and I also have the full responsibilities for a wife and children. But my mind is forever concentrated on God. I am forever scared that if even for a fraction of a second my mind wanders away from God then death will come to me instantly! This is why I am called Videhi."

The king then had a feast prepared for the Brahmins. He gave them a gift of a thousand rupees each. Before bidding them farewell he said, "If I had told you why I am Videhi when you asked you would not have believed me. Just as your hearts pounded faster, my heart constantly beats fast, because even though I am king of the whole earth, I'm aware that death may come any time."

The Brahmins were pleased with the answer.

We also live in this world. If our minds are constantly focused on God and we have firm faith and shelter in our Guru and God, and if we obey their commands implicitly and offer correct worship, then God will forever care for us.

THE OLD LADY'S BONES

There was an old lady. She sinned everyday. She would kill ants and mosquitoes. She never gave food to beggars and always beat the poor. She would even beat Brahmins and dumb animals. She would hit anyone and everyone. Even when her son asked her not to she would. And when the sinful old lady died her soul went to hell.

Her son knew that his mother had gone to hell and so he thought of saving her in some way. He decided to consecrate his mother's bones in the Ganga and so liberate her. With this thought he tied the old lady's bones in a piece of cloth and wearing white clothes set off for Kashi. Many people go to Kashi as pilgrims. He walked for two months before he finally got there.

Ganga thought to herself, "If the son throws the sinful old lady's bones into me I shall be burdened with sin. And then who will save me?" In the meantime the son placed his mother's bones by the riverside and went to answer a call of nature. Gangaji took this chance and taking the form of a bird grabbed the bag of bones and flew to the son's home and put the bones on the roof.

Returning to the riverside the son began to search for the bones. He looked everywhere but couldn't find the bag. He began asking everyone, "Who has stolen my bag?" Everyone asked, "What was in it?" He replied,

"My mother's bones. I wanted to throw them into Ganga." They all wondered who would take the bones and began searching the riverside to help him but could find nothing.

The son started walking home very sad. As soon as he got there he saw the bag. And when he opened it, there were the bones! Who brought them here he thought to himself. He really was puzzled.

He stayed at home for ten days and then set off for Kashi once again. After walking for fifty days he arrived at his Brahmin friend's home. He decided to stay the night. The Brahmin owned a cow. Everyday the Brahmin's wife would hit the cow twice with a stick and then milk it. The poor cow was very unhappy. That night she told her calf, "If the Brahmin's wife beats me today I'll stab and kill the Brahmin's son with my horns in the morning."

The calf replied, "If you kill the boy you will have the sin of killing a Brahmin on your head and so you will turn black in colour!"

The cow replied, "There is a river by this village where holy sadhus bathe daily. I'll dip myself in the river and purify myself, but I can no longer tolerate this harassment."

The old lady's son was sleeping nearby. He heard everything the cow said. In the morning the cow killed the Brahmin's son. Because of the sin the cow turned black. The cow left the house and started walking to the river. The old lady's son carrying his mother's bones followed the cow. At the river the cow walked into the water where the sadhus bathed. When she climbed out on the opposite side she was white and purified. The son was watching all this. He threw his mother's bones into the river. At once his mother appeared to him and said, "I have been saved!"

Our souls can only be purified and liberated by the grace and strength of a true Sadhu.

THE SESAME SCHOLAR

There was once a Brahmin. He began to study Sanskrit. But he didn't have a very good memory. He could never memorise anything. He would try, but then he would quickly forget.

One day he filled a large bowl with sesame seeds. Next to this he placed a gourd. Then he said a Sanskrit word and put a sesame seed in the gourd. He repeated the word and placed another seed in the gourd. In this way he filled the gourd repeating the same Sanskrit word over and over. He then emptied the gourd and began repeating another word. This was his daily routine.

After some time he became a great Sanskrit scholar. He would defeat others in debates on the scriptures. Whenever a scholar from another place came for a debate the people always selected the Brahmin to speak for them. They knew he would win the debate. He was very clever. Everyone called him the *tal-tumbdi shastri* – the sesame scholar.

We should also study with courage and determination. Never say, "I can never learn this. I can't remember anything." Always look to the *tal-tumbdi shastri* for inspiration.

TUMBARU AND NARAD

Narad and Tumbaru went before God to Vaikunth. Tumbaru was a very good singer. He sang so well before the Lord that even the Lord felt joy and peace in his heart.

As a gift the Lord gave him some fine clothes and ornaments.

Even though Naradji is considered the 'mind of God,' as he is a great devotee, he felt jealous of Tumbaru. He decided to learn to sing and please the Lord. His voice wasn't very good but he learnt how to sing anyway. Naradji then went before God and sang.

The Lord said, "You've come to get fine clothes and ornaments but you can't sing as well as Tumbaru." The Lord was very clear!

Naradji then performed austerities to please Shivji. He did *dharna-parna*, and asked a boon that he become an expert singer.

But when he next sang before the Lord it was to no avail. God was not pleased.

Naradji again began to practice. He worked very hard for thousands of years. But as he was doing this out of jealousy, God was not pleased.

In the end he went to Tumbaru. Naradji became humble and asked Tumbaru to teach him how to sing.

Tumbaru taught him. Naradji then sang before the Lord in Dwarka. The

Lord was extremely pleased and rewarded Naradji with clothes and ornaments. Never be jealous. Strive to learn from those who are better than us.

THE GODDESS'S SHADOW

There was a thief. He had taken a vow never to listen to spiritual discourses. One day the thief was walking past the village square. There, a Brahmin was discoursing on the Devi Puran. The thief covered his ears and hurried on. But in his haste he trod on a thorn, and had to stop and pick it out with his hand. In that time he heard a few words of the Brahmin's discourse. The Brahmin was describing that a goddess has no shadow. The thief remembered these words.

After a few days the thief and three others robbed the king's treasury. When the king found out he decided on a cunning plan to find the real thieves. The king knew that thieves were very scared of goddesses, so he had a court dancing girl dressed up as a goddess and sent her to the area where most of the thieves lived.

With her hair loose and dressed to look exactly like a goddess, the girl approached the thieves and said in a weird voice, "Who has looted the king's treasury. Tell me the truth at once or I will curse you all."

All the thieves were frightened. But the thief who had accidently heard a few words of a spiritual discourse remembered that a "goddess never has a shadow." So he told the other thieves, "Take a candle near her, and if she is a real goddess then she will have no shadow." They held a candle close to her and at once saw a shadow. And so there and then they punished the dancing girl. She barely escaped with her life!

In this way, just a few words of spiritual discourse heard in passing saved the thieves' lives and earned them some wealth.

Then the thief thought to himself, "If I profited so much just by listening to a few words of spiritual discourse then how much more will I gain if I listen to more spiritual discourse!" Thus, he gave up his life of stealing and began to lead a good and honest life.

We should regularly listen to spiritual discourse. The benefits are great.

A POTTER WINS THE LOTTERY

In a village there lived a potter. He once gambled one rupee in a lottery. He struck lucky. The lottery man told him, "You've won 30,000 rupees."

The potter asked, "Where's the money?"

The lottery man gave him the stacks of money totalling 30,000 rupees.

The potter had never before in his life seen even five rupees. And so seeing all this money his mind went wild. He became a lunatic!

The village folk wondered, "What shall we do now?" Some clever villagers found an answer.

They took the potter to a big bank and there in the safe showed him the stacks of hundreds of thousands of rupees. The potter was amazed. He said, "In front of all this money my 30,000 rupees is nothing!" His mind became normal again.

If the great Sadhu reveals the greatness and prominent status we enjoyed in our last lives we wouldn't obey him in the least. Even we'd go mad. Attaining Satsang is comparable to winning Akshardham in a lottery.

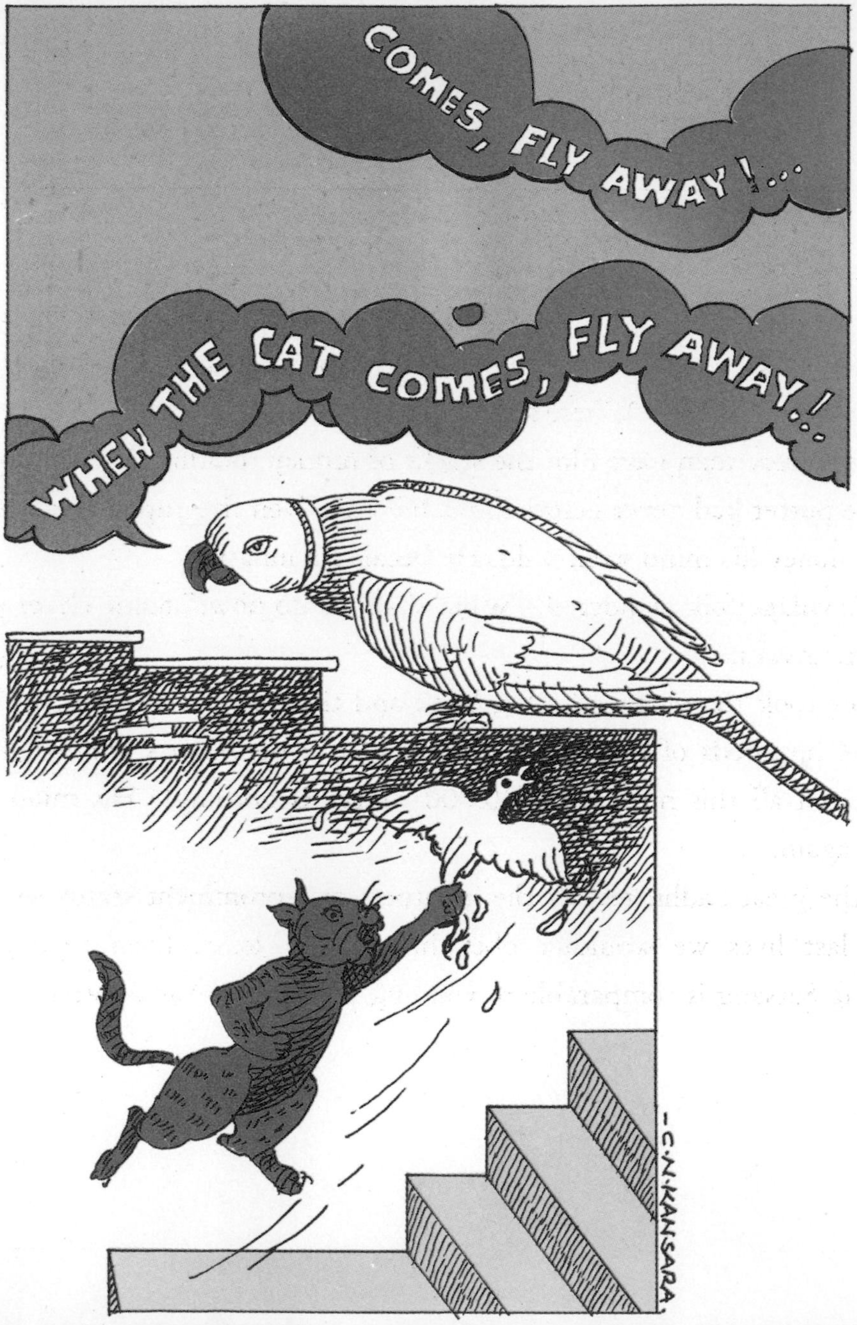
WHEN THE CAT COMES, FLY AWAY!.!
COMES, FLY AWAY!...
-C.N.KANSARA.

FLY AWAY WHEN A CAT COMES

One wealthy man was very fond of pets, especially parrots. He brought home a new parrot and began teaching it to talk. The very first survival lesson was, "Fly away when a cat comes." He said it aloud a few times and made the parrot repeat it. Within a short time the parrot learnt it by heart and for the whole day repeated it non stop, "Fly away when a cat comes. Fly away when a cat comes."

One day it so happened, that a real cat came. It stealthily approached the parrot who was busy repeating the phrase. The cat lifted its paws to pounce on it. The parrot dumbly rehearsed the phrase, "Fly away when a cat comes," but did not fly away.

The cat attacked and killed the bird in mid-sentence.

It is true that the man had taught the parrot, "Fly away when a cat comes," but he had not shown the parrot what a cat is by showing him a real cat. The poor parrot knew very well that he should beware of cats, but he didn't know what a cat looked like.

In spiritual life we are taught to beware of evils, but we should also clearly understand and recognise the forms in which they come to tempt us. Similarly, on the positive side, the whole Satsang Fellowship says that "Bhagwan

Swaminarayan is the God Supreme." We repeat it again and again. But without having the true understanding of who Bhagwan Swaminarayan is, and what is meant by God Supreme, we are not likely to attain the fullest benefits. This practical differentiation of good and evil is given by the true Sadhu alone.

THE SICK MAN'S BED IS INSIDE

Once there was an old woman. She lived with her one and only son. One day, the son caught a serious illness. The old woman was very fond of her son and so prepared his bed inside the house to provide extra care, while she slept outside.

One night, a buffalo, which had run loose in the village, came to where the old woman was sleeping. The buffalo had an itch and began scratching its head against the leg of the bed. Its force rocked the bed and startled the old woman from her sleep. She saw the buffalo and was shocked. She remembered hearing in the religious discourses that the Lord of Death comes on a buffalo to collect people at the time of their death.

She thought very quickly, "Since my son is very ill, it is certain that the Lord of Death has come to take him away, but by mistake, he seems to be pulling my bed." She at once spoke out, "Look, I'm quite well. The sick man's bed is inside."

This amply shows the selfishness of worldly relationships. One must rise above them and worship God.

THE GHOST AND THE POLE

One man learnt black magic and summoned a ghost. Through mantras and rituals he managed to keep full control over the ghost, which obediently carried out all his commands. One by one he got his jobs done by it. But there was one problem. The moment the ghost finished one job he had to be given another. If for a moment he remained free he would prepare to attack his master saying, "Give me more work or I'll devour you!"

It was alright for a few days; there was enough work to do, but then, it became exceedingly difficult to keep the ghost busy. The man grew worried and began fearing for his own life. "Oh God," he thought, "what shall I do? If I do not find him enough work, I'm a dead man. But how can I find work upon work everyday?"

His body took great toll and thinned in the growing tension. He himself was busy in search of new work for the ghost. Everything seemed to have gone wrong. Just then, in the middle of this trouble, he met a sadhu. The sadhu showed him a way out. The man happily obeyed the sadhu and ordered the ghost, "Go and bring me the tallest bamboo from the jungle of Gir."

Instantly, the ghost left and accomplished the task given. Next, he said, "Erect the pole in the centre of the courtyard by driving it deep into the ground."

This too was done quickly.

"Now what?" the ghost demanded.

"Now, climb up and down this pole continuously, until I call you for something else," the man ordered.

Yes, it certainly kept the ghost busy. There was no end to it. Then the man relaxed. Whenever he needed a hand for farming, or harvesting or watering or building, he called the ghost and then sent it back to the pole.

Our mind is like the ghost. If it remains idle, then it brings great harm to us. So keep it busy with reading one scripture after another. Read the Bhaktachintamani, Vachanamrut, and Swamini Vato. Keep remembering and reflecting upon the memories and incidents of Shastriji Maharaj and also the divine incidents of God. Then, even in your sleep and dreams you shall see these divine episodes. In this way our mind will eventually become pure and desireless.

sensical order.

"Go out and buy the most expensive thing in this place."

It so happened, that in Java, things like gold, pearls, jewels and ornaments were being sold at a very low price, because they were in abundance. The minister advised, "Master, let us purchase these here and we can make a bumper profit back at home by selling them at a high price."

"No, No! We must not buy cheap things."

So they kept hunting for the most expensive item on sale in the market. And you won't believe it, but the most expensive things on the whole of Java island were stones! Yes, stones!

"Minister, invest all our money in buying these stones," ordered the son.

"But Master, at home, in Kathiawad, we have plenty of stones such as these. They are worthless. Instead, let us purchase the gold and jewellery."

But the son remained stubborn. He would not budge from his foolishness. He spent six years searching for and collecting stones. All his advisors silently watched in horror as the three ships were loaded with stones of varying shapes and sizes. Finally, with the air of a victorious commander, the son ordered his crew for the journey home.

Back at home, everyone was eagerly awaiting the return of the expedition. The foolish son had proudly sent a message in advance, "Dear father, I am bringing back three shiploads of priceless goods."

The news brought a wave of excitement in the father's heart. He spread the news to everyone in town and boasted about his son's twelve year long enterprise. At night he dreamt about diamonds and jewels, gold and silver... "Oh my! Three ships overflowing with wealth!" he thought. The father spent his days dreaming and his nights talking. After three years, the day of celebration came. The ships pulled into harbour. Every man alive rushed to the coast; some had come to congratulate; some were curious to see the riches; and some were there to be the first to buy the goods before they even reached the market.

They asked, "What goods have you brought?"

"Stones!" replied the son with pride.

"Come on, don't make jokes," they challenged in quiet disbelief. Nobody took him seriously and they all went to the giant assembly his father had arranged for his son's reception.

Father and son embraced each other, the whole family celebrated the reunion. Then the Sheth asked, "O son, the great adventurer, what have you brought to our people from the far lands?"

"Stones!"

"I am 92 years old. I have enough experience in these matters. So stop fooling and tell us the truth," the father lovingly admonished.

"Honestly, father, I have brought shiploads of stones. These smooth stones were the most expensive things on the island."

So saying, he ordered his men to unload some samples. The whole assembly was shocked into silence. Some people were horrified, others laughed.

The son's foolishness had been exposed. His dumbheadedness cut a sorry figure of his father. The family's reputation had received a severe blow, ruining it forever.

And at the end of it all, the stones had to be thrown deep into the sea because they were too circular to be of any use even in building houses!

Likewise, when we leave our body and sail home to heaven, God will come forth to receive us. He will ask us what wealth we have earned for our soul. We may reply with a list, "A three-storey house, a few children, and thousands of rupees." This is called material wealth.

Collecting material wealth is like gathering stones. It is of no value at all. Only when we spend our life enriching our soul and striving for salvation by collecting the inner wealth of knowledge will our journey to earth become worthwhile.

THE DONKEY AND THE OX

Two *bawas* went to a village. They decided to rest in the village centre under a tree. One *bawa* went for a bath.

In that time a devout man came near the *bawa* under the tree and asked, "What is that other *bawa* who has gone for a bath like?"

"The fellow's a donkey!" the *bawa* answered quickly.

When the other *bawa* returned from his bath the *bawa* resting under the tree went for a bath. The devout man now asked the bathed *bawa*, "What is that other *bawa* who has gone for a bath like?"

"The fellow's an ox!" the *bawa* cried. When both *bawas* were bathed and ready the devout man invited them to his home for lunch. Both accepted and reached there at twelve o'clock. They sat down ready with their bowls.

Now, this devout man was also very clever. In one bowl he served oats and in the other he placed mixed wheat and barley grains. The *bawas* became angry. They said, "What are you doing? How can we eat this?"

The devout man said, "For the one who is a donkey there are oats and for the ox there is wheat and barley. Please do begin to eat."

The *bawas* were furious.

But the devout man told them off, "Learn the virtues of the person you stay with. How can you call one another a donkey or an ox?" he scolded.

He taught them a lesson. After a while the man served the *bawas* delicious *puri* and *dudhpak* which he had prepared earlier.

Singing the virtues of another is true devotion.

THE SKILL OF A SANNYASI

One sannyasi reached the age of eighty. In his worldly life, before renouncing, he had belonged to the Brahmin caste and had possessed a sly nature for starting quarrels.

He went to the house of a Patel family. He was warmly welcomed and given accommodation. He thought whilst relaxing, "I wonder if I still possess my skill for stirring up fights?"

The man of the house, Mr. Patel, was out ploughing his fields. Only his wife and his sister were at home. The sannyasi called Mrs. Patel to one corner and said, "Your husband and his sister have an immoral relationship."

"No, no, a brother and sister would never indulge in adultery," Mrs. Patel doubted.

"If you don't believe me, then stay up tonight and see for yourself," the sannyasi advised.

Next, he approached the sister saying, "Your brother is a drunkard."

"No, no my brother could never be a drunkard." The sister refused to believe him.

"If you doubt me, then check for yourself. Tonight, when he's fast asleep, go and smell his breath."

Evening came and the farmer Patel returned home from a long day's work. He was pleased to see a holy sannyasi at his home. After exchanging greetings, the sannyasi wore a serious face and disclosed to the Patel, "I have noticed in this short stay at your house that your sister is a witch."

Shocked, the Patel replied, "No, not my sister!"

"Yes, yes your very own sister! Stay awake tonight. Watch her, she will come sniffing at your mouth."

The sannyasi misguided and sowed strong suspicions in their minds while he spread his bed and relaxed, waiting for the show to begin.

Night fell. Each member of the house pretended to be asleep. At twelve midnight, the sister got up to check whether her brother was a drunk. She silently crept into his bedroom and by his bed lowered her nose to smell his breath. The Patel was lying awake and he jumped up shouting, "You witch!" Meanwhile, the wife saw her husband and his sister together and roared, "You beasts! Adulterers!" The sister was shocked at such chaos. Her doubts were confirmed. "You drunkard, you've been drinking," she shouted.

And so a great row erupted. Each one shouting at the top of his or her voice, refusing to hear the other. The sannyasi, quietly enjoyed the spectacle, congratulating himself for not having forgotten his skill. Then he interrupted them, calmed them and said, "Do not fight amongst yourself. It is no one's fault at all. It's just that I was trying out my old skills."

One must give up the habit of stirring up quarrels. It creates trouble and unrest to many people. What good would it do us to disturb the lives of others? Be helpful to others, not harmful.

NEVER HIDE YOUR GURU

There was once a son of a Garasiyo. Six kilometres away from his village was a lake. The boy would always take the cows to graze by the lake shore. Cranes lived in the lake. Standing in shallow water they would catch any fish that came their way. But water would also fill their beaks. So they would throw the fish high into the air and in the meantime empty their mouths. The crane would catch the fish just before it fell back into the water.

The Garasiyo's son was clever. Watching the cranes catch fish he thought to himself, "It would be worthwhile learning this." With him he had a stick. He threw it up into the air and caught it in his mouth. It didn't hurt. He began to practice everyday. After a while he started to throw a dagger and learned to catch it in his mouth. In this way after about twelve months he learnt how to throw a sword up into the air and catch it in his mouth. He would catch it in such a way that he wouldn't cut himself in the slightest.

Once in the kingdom came a group of *bhavaiyas*. They performed many tricks and feats before the king. Last of all, a sword was thrown into the air and one of them caught it in his mouth. The king was impressed. He thought, "This is a game of death. He must have learnt the trick from a great guru."

The king said to the *bhavaiyas*, "None else can perform such a feat. I'm very pleased. Tomorrow morning come to collect a 1,000 rupee prize."

The Garasiyo's son was also watching all this. He said, "Even I can perform this feat."

The king was surprised, "Show it to us then," he commanded.

The boy had practised everyday. So he threw up the sword and easily caught it in his mouth. He wasn't hurt in the least.

The king saw this. He thought, "This is something everyone can learn. I won't give the *bhavaiyas* a prize now."

Because of the boy the *bhavaiyas* lost their prize money. They told him, "We'd like to see you tomorrow morning."

In the morning the *bhavaiyas* sought out the boy's house. "Because of you we've lost our prize. But tell us, from whom did you learn this feat. Who is your guru?" they questioned.

The boy said, "I have no guru. I've learnt the trick by myself. He didn't say, "I learnt the feat from a crane." He hid his guru.

The *bhavaiyas* said, "Without a guru this feat can never be learnt. If you try to perform this feat without a guru to help you, you'd cut your throat. Don't hide your guru. Tell us who he is."

The *bhavaiyas* tried for over an hour but the boy wouldn't reveal his guru. He repeated, "I've learnt the feat by myself." Finally the *bhavaiyas* said, "We'd like to learn to perfect the feat from you. So please throw up a sword and catch it."

The Garasiyo's son threw up the sword, but this time he couldn't catch it in his mouth. The sword came down on his throat and cut it!

The boy hid his guru only to have his throat cut. If he had simply said, "My guru is a crane. I saw it throw up a fish and catch it. So I first practiced with a stick and then a dagger and then a sword," he wouldn't have died. By hiding his guru he had to suffer the consequences.

We should never hide our guru. From the guru we learn *brahmavidya*. Such a guru is called Gunatit.

BEATING UP DARKNESS

In a village lived several Koli Patels. They were very foolish. They once thought to themselves, "For many years now darkness at night time has slipped into our houses. Let's keep a strict guard today and make sure darkness doesn't creep in. One Patel picked up a stick, another a washing bat, another a pestle or dustpan to chase darkness out just in case it did manage to gain entry. And so at six o'clock in the evening the villagers finished dinner and sat ready on their cots outside their homes. They watched the sunset, carefully watching around them lest darkness sneaked into their homes.

Slowly the sun set. One man went into his home for a drink of water at 6.30 pm He raised the alarm, "Get up! Get up! What are you watching outside for? Darkness has already sneaked in!"

All the Patels grabbed their sticks, washing bats and dustpans. They began to beat darkness in the house. In the darkness they broke many pots and pans. Many of the Patels themselves were hit on the head! They spent the whole night trying to chase darkness away. With the coming of morning the sun rose and darkness went away. The Patels stroked their moustaches with pride and happily said, "We really did beat it away." They all became very sure of themselves.

Beating darkness doesn't chase it away. The rising sun causes darkness to go.

People decide for themselves what salvation is — as the Patels thought of darkness. Freedom from the cycle of births and deaths is true salvation. Without a sun-like true Guru our ignorance is never driven away.

People suffer hardships in their worldly life and yet believe that they've made life easier! No matter how much you may improve your worldly life at the core it is rotten.

FORCE 99

There once lived a *sheth* who was a wealthy businessman. Next to him lived a poor man who sweated out his whole day in hard labour. In fact, his whole family – wife and children – worked hard at menial jobs. Whatever they earned, they spent. After their daily supper, they would relax and pray to God, then retire comfortably to sleep. Next morning, they would rise, pray to God and go off to work. Yet they were content, happy and relaxed.

On the other hand, the wealthy *sheth* was always edgy, hasty and tense. He would not even spend money on decent food. His only desire was to earn money – to collect more and more of it. And so he never found time free to relax or enjoy life.

One day, the *sheth's* wife complained, "Look at the poor man and his family next door. They earn very little, yet they live happily. They eat well, pray well and enjoy life together. Whereas we have much and yet enjoy not a moment of peace!"

The *sheth* readily replied, "He has not yet encountered Force 99, and so he lives peacefully."

"What's Force 99?" the wife inquired.

"I'll show you soon when the time comes," the *sheth* answered.

That very night, the *sheth* packed a small bag with 99 rupees and threw it into the hut of his neighbour. Next morning when the family awoke, they saw the bag. They opened it and counted the money! Then the couple thought, "If we save one rupee then it would make a complete hundred!" From then onwards to save that one rupee they began to go out to work very early and return late at night. Tired and exhausted, they would go straight to bed without a word! They cut down on food to save money. When after some days a rupee was saved, they thought, "If we work hard like this we should be able to save 100 rupees every year!"

And so their greed grew. They began work before sunrise and returned home late in the dark. They ate less and cheap food. And even stopped their daily prayers.

The *sheth's* wife noticed this. "The labourers are no longer to be seen in their home. They never relax or pray! What on earth has happened to them?" she asked.

The *sheth* explained, "Did I not tell you that when Force 99 hits you, this happens. They've just been struck by Force 99!"

If we are struck by Force 99, the drive to just earn money, to gather more and more, we lose our peace. Hence, he who is content and satisfied is the wealthiest of all.

THE GARASIYO AND THE GHANCHI

In a village lived a Garasiyo and a Ghanchi. The Garasiyo was very thin. The Ghanchi was fat. The wives of both men would quarrel. The Ghanchi's wife would say, "How plump my husband is. Your husband's so skinny!" and hold her head up high. The Garasiyo's wife would reply, "My husband may be skinny but he will one day work a wonder." But the Ghanchi's wife would taunt in reply, "Huh, what can your bony and skinny husband do?"

One day the village was attacked by a gang of plunderers. The war horn was blown and all the Garasiyos prepared to fight. The skinny Garasiyo also readied himself. Hearing the war horn he was filled with valour. His wife told him, "The Ghanchi's wife teases me everyday and yet you do nothing about it. Before you go to fight and protect the village go teach him a lesson." The Garasiyo really was feeling brave today. He strode off to the Ghanchi's house who was engrossed in work. Next to him was an iron crowbar weighing several kilos. The Garasiyo picked up the crowbar and twisted it around the Ghanchi's neck. He then immediately went off to fight. The Ghanchi was left wondering what had happened to him!

The Garasiyos won the fight. And so the skinny Garasiyo returned home triumphant.

But the Ghanchi now had a heavy necklace around his neck. He tried very hard to take it off but couldn't. Finally, the frustrated Ghanchi told his wife, "Go and ask the Garasiyo to come and take this crowbar off me."

In the morning the Ghanchi's wife went to the Garasiyo's wife and said, "Tell your husband to come and take the crowbar off my husband's neck." The Garasiyo's wife replied with a cunning smile, "What can my skinny husband do?"

The Ghanchi's wife was sorry but what could she do now? The Garasiyo's wife then felt a little sorry for the Ghanchi and so said, "Not now, but when there's another raid we'll see."

The heavy necklace hung from the Ghanchi's neck. It was very troublesome, he couldn't even eat or sleep properly. Then one day there was another attack on the village. The battle horn was sounded. The Garasiyos prepared themselves to fight. The skinny Garasiyo was filled with valour again. His wife told him, "Take the crowbar off the Ghanchi's neck before you go to fight today!" The skinny Garasiyo went to the Ghanchi's house and in one effort twisted the crowbar straight again and took it off from around the Ghanchi's neck. He then went off to protect the village.

It is only when we become brave that we achieve our goals. The time to fight has come. Infatuation, ego, envy, etc. are all to be fought against. Become brave and kill the evil instincts, such as, sexual desires, anger, etc. Our Guru has blown the battle horn. Prepare at once.

BUMBLE BEE AND WORM

There was a very close friendship between a bumble bee and a worm. Once the bee said to the worm, "Why do you live in muck and faeces? Come to my garden. There are roses and agaves and jasmines. You'll be thrilled by their fragrance."

The worm gave it a serious thought, "I'll go and visit his garden, but what if there's nothing to eat there? I may starve to death." As a precaution he rolled up two small balls of dirt and faeces and plugged them into his nostrils. The bumble bee, unaware of this, asked him to climb onto his back. Off they flew. In the garden the air was sweet with fragrance. The bee placed the worm on top of a rose and asked, "Well, what do you think of the fragrance?"

"Nothing special. I still smell the same old odour," the worm retorted, not impressed at all.

The bee was confused, "Why does my friend fail to enjoy the fragrance?" he asked himself. Then he took a closer look at the worm and found two tiny balls of faeces fitted in his nostrils. He made a plan for removing them. Taking the worm to a pool of water, he offered him the chance to swim. They both dived into the water. The bee then climbed upon the worm's back and pushed his head underwater. Water rushed into the worm's nose and mouth and made him burst out with violent sneezing. This procedure forced out the mess that was blocking the worm's nose. Quickly picking up the worm the bee returned to the rose, "Ah... Ah... what a scent! It's fabulous... The scent of rose is wonderful." The worm praised the flowers to no end.

"The fragrance was always here, but it was you who chose not to enjoy it. You had stuffed your nose with muck and excreta," the bee scolded his friend, and then took him to savour the scents of other flowers in the garden.

This is what happens when people come to sit in the spiritual assemblies or come to serve the enlightened Sadhu for wisdom. They come to the divine atmosphere fragrant with the goodness of God, but have secretly filled their hearts with filth and desires of the world. Therefore, even while sitting in spiritual discourses, they smell the odour of the world. It is when the enlightened Sadhu splashes him in the ocean of wisdom and cleanses him of this world's mess that he enjoys the happiness of God.

THE DEVOTEE AND THE THIEF

There was a devotee. Once he stayed up all night in a *bhajan* programme and was walking home. His eyes were red due to lack of sleep.

There was also a thief. He had tried all night to steal something but had not succeeded. Disappointed, he was now returning home. His eyes were also red due to lack of sleep.

The two saw each other on the road home. Both had red eyes. The thief thought to himself, "He seems to be a thief like myself, and it seems he, too, stayed up all night without getting any loot. That's why his eyes are red."

The devotee thought to himself, "This man has probably spent the whole night singing *bhajans* like me, no wonder his eyes are red!"

The thief thought the devotee to be a thief. The devotee thought the thief to be a devotee.

One who has jaundice sees only yellow! A person with only God in his eyes sees goodness and virtue everywhere.

AN IMPOSTER GURU

There was an imposter guru. He regularly faked samadhi and fooled innocent people in every village he visited. When someone asked him, "O Master, can you tell me where my father has gone after his death?" the guru would boast of his powers saying, "Wait, I'll go into deep samadhi and search for him."

Then he would stage a show of samadhi and pretend to speak with a transcendental vision, "Your father, yes I see him sitting in the assembly of heaven." The gullible neither questioned nor doubted his hypocrisy.

But one day, a sharp young fellow asked, "Dear guruji, where has my father gone?"

The guruji summoned all his energies and entered samadhi, "Your father, is sitting in Vaikunth, the abode of Lord Ram."

"Will you please bring him here," the young man asked.

"No, no! You cannot call him here from there."

"If you are incapable then shall I call him?" So saying the boy shouted, "Father!"

And there, alive and well, sitting in the group of people before the guru, his father stood up, "Here I am, son!"

The hyprocrisy of the guru was publicly exposed.

Bhagwan Swaminarayan has always condemned hypocrisy. It is better to have little but true devotion and never fall into the trap of faking virtues.

THE UGLY MAN AND THE MIRROR

There lived a very ugly man, his face was dark and distorted. Once he came across a mirror and looked into it. He was shocked to see his ugly face and flared up into a rage. "Oh you! You have spoilt my face." He smashed the mirror against a stone.

But what was the fault of the mirror? It only showed him what he really was. Satsang – the company of the enlightened Sadhu – is like a mirror. It reveals to us what we really are. All our weaknesses and ugliness of anger, lust, greed, etc. are exposed. And if you find yourself finding fault with the Sadhu, always remember he is faultless like the mirror, it is only our faults that we see reflected in his pure being.

A CLEVER WISH

Baniyas are very clever people. One Baniya was blind and poor and so nobody married him. He set out to appease God by performing severe austerities. After months of effort, God was pleased on him and offered, "Ask any one blessing from me. I shall grant you the blessing, but it should be only one."

The Baniya was puzzled and confused. He struggled with his intelligence, "If I ask for my eyes, what use are they if I remain a beggar and bachelor for life."

"If I ask for wealth. Still nobody will marry a blind man."

"And of what use is asking for a wife, if all my life I remain a poor, blind man."

He wanted all three and God had commanded him to ask for only one.

But the Baniya was very clever. He took his time and then spoke.

"O God, I do not want anything else except this one thing. That in my seven-storey house, I desire to see with my very own eyes, the wife of my middle son churning buttermilk with a golden whisk."

In this one prayer, he received his eyesight, a wife, three sons and an abundance of wealth.

Similarly, when we ask God to grant us salvation and keep us in His service forever, eternal happiness is included in this one prayer.

THE MONKEY, THE SNAKE AND THE GOAT

A snake charmer moved from village to village to entertain folks with his acrobatic team of a monkey, a snake and a goat.

Once, while wading across a river, he balanced the snake basket on his head, sat the monkey on his shoulder and guided the goat with his hand. The water level was low but there flowed a strong current. The charmer cautiously took his steps, with an eye on all three of his team.

Midway, where the force was fierce enough to drag away the goat, he tightened his grip on it. The other two were safe above. Or were they?

The monkey, by nature, was mischievous. It was restless and couldn't resist playing a game. It slowly opened the snake basket. The snake, from the darkness of the basket, sprung up with its head high and tongue hissing... sss... sss... sss. The sound and fury, frightened the monkey and it fell into the water. The current began to drag the monkey away. A split-second effort to save the monkey threw the charmer off balance and he dropped the snake basket into the stream. To catch hold of the basket, he lost his grip on the goat. Within seconds, all three of his companions – the monkey, the snake and the goat were carried away by the current.

In real life, our mind is the monkey. It is restless and difficult to predict. Many times it causes trouble and leads us into serious trouble. Instead of helping us float across the ocean of life, it throws us into the ocean. Therefore, it is wise that we control and master our mind.

STRANGE MEMORIAL STONES

One Brahmin was passing through hard times. He found it difficult to survive and maintain his family in his own village. So he decided to look for a prosperous place to resettle. During his search he arrived at the outskirts of a very pious-looking village. On entering it, he noticed a strange scene. Many memorial stones had been erected in memory of the dead. This was normal. The bizarreness was that the lifespan of each deceased person was beautifully written in gold foil: 'He lived for two years', 'He died at the age of three,' 'She survived for two-and-a-half years.'

"My God!" the Brahmin worried, "People in this village don't live long. What use is it to settle in a place where one is destined to die quickly."

He was about to leave in haste when the village folk saw him. They welcomed him to their homes, served him delicacies to eat and made him comfortable. Their genuine hospitality won his confidence. But the question of death at a young age was gnawing at him non-stop. When evening came, the whole village turned out for the spiritual discourse. They had come with books and diaries to make notes. They listened to every word spoken with unbroken attention. The Brahmin was convinced of their piety and was eager to settle there. It seemed like a holy paradise – except for those lifespans on the memorial stones. They robbed him of all joy and depressed him. He stayed in the village for a few days but never quite got over his gloom.

One day, one of the villagers questioned his sadness. He confided his worries, "I am touched by your love and hospitality. You are good pious people. I also wish to settle here with my family. But what good would it do to us if we are to die within a few years?"

"What makes you think this way?"

"Not just think, I've read those memorial stones on the village outskirts. Not one person seems to have lived more than five years!"

The villager laughed and said, "You are learned but not wise. Just look at my father. He's sixty-years-old. If everyone here died by the age of two or three then why would he still be healthy at sixty?" He pointed at his father and then at other old people in the village.

"Then, what is one to understand by the lifespans on the memorial stones?" the Brahmin questioned.

"It is a custom in this village," the villager explained, "that whenever we sit in a spiritual discourse each one of us notes down his or her time spent in the discourse in a personal diary. Perhaps you have noticed this in the past few days you've been with us." The Brahmin nodded and the man continued, "Well, we believe that our real lifespan is only that which we spend in spiritual discourses. If a man spends one hour a day in the discourses, then it is thirty hours or one and one quarter days per month. By the end of one year he has said to have lived for fifteen days. And even if he survives for sixty years, his life comes round to about two-and-a-half years. This is how the lifespan is calculated."

We must also think in this manner. Only that part of our life which we have spent in worshipping God has been really lived. The years spent in worldly activities have gone to waste. All of us should pass more and more time in spiritual discourses and God's work. Gunatitanand Swami often asked the devotees to donate a part of their lifespan for spiritual activities. In twelve months, one full month should be spent in the company of the true Sadhu, listening to his wisdom and serving him through mind, word and deed. This is what will add up to make our real lifespan.

DEVOTION WITHOUT PURPOSE

There was a Brahmin. He had seven sons. In the yard in front of their house stood a pipal tree. Underneath the tree was a Shivling. The Brahmin worshipped here everyday.

One day he had to go to another village. He told his sons, "Worship the Shivling tomorrow morning for me. I have to go out." The Brahmin then left. He returned the next evening.

He asked his sons, "Did you do that work I gave you."

"No," answered his sons.

"Do I always have to do that chore!" the Brahmin complained.

Never believe worship of God to be a chore. God is pleased with us if we worship Him with love and enthusiasm. Devotion offered as a chore is without purpose.

NIGHT COMPLAINS TO GOD

Once, night came into the court of God and kneeled before the Lord. She was breathless and was distraught with misery.

"It's Day," she complained, "He follows me. Everywhere I go he drives me out. He's after my life and puts me to great suffering. It's unfair, O Lord, please have mercy upon me and do justice."

"Both of you come together in my court and I shall let justice prevail," God commanded.

The Lord knew that Night and Day can never come together, and so there was no question of a trial.

It is as clear as day and night that where there is the light of God and His true Sadhu, there can never exist the darkness of ignorance.

ADU OR NADU?

A farmer was travelling along a dusty road in his cart. He was a Patel by surname. On the way he gave a lift to Mr. Voraji. Now, Voraji was naive in nature and lacked commonsense.

The roads in those times were more like trails dotted with bumps and holes. On seeing a large hole ahead, the Patel warned, "Voraji, hold the *adu* (the side panel) of the cart tightly, there's a giant hole coming up ahead. Our cart is in for a big jolt."

Voraji heard *nadu* instead of *adu* and closed his two hands round the *nadu* (string around the waist) of his trousers. Voraji held it tightly with his hands. And when the hole came, and the cart jerked, Voraji was flung out of the cart onto the road. He landed on his back squirming with pain and bruises. His back half-broken, he shouted at the Patel who turned around with surprise. The Patel stopped the cart and helped Voraji up and consoled him.

"But didn't I tell you to hold the *adu* of the cart? I did warn you of the violent jolt..."

Voraji interrupted with a complaining voice. "But I never let go of the *nadu*. I am still holding onto it, even now." He showed the *nadu* of his trousers to the Patel. It was clasped tightly with both of his hands. The Patel burst out laughing.

"Oh Voraji! I told you to hold the *adu* of the cart not your *nadu*."

And he continued to laugh endlessly.

The story emphasises the need for clear understanding. If there is the slightest error in understanding then we may break our backs in the spiritual world. A great many people misunderstand reality and hold onto the *nadu* like Mr. Voraji. And even when they suffer and are exploited they still never forsake their obstinacy. Everyone wants to worship God, but he who spends time and clearly understands the spiritual essence is of a special class. It is no use being like the fools who misunderstand and defy the words of a true Sadhu.

A HORSE BREAKS A LEG

A horse once had a dream in which he had an accident that broke his leg. Long after waking, the horse remained seated because he was convinced that his leg was injured. Nothing was wrong, except that his dream had carried a great impact on his thinking. Even when forced to stand up, he stood steady on three legs, while holding his fourth leg limp and loose. The owner couldn't make the horse move an inch, let alone make it trot. Puzzled and confused, the owner called a vet, and said, "This horse is healthy and strong. Nothing's wrong with him. He's not ill nor hurt. The only thing is that he has a limp leg and refuses to walk. He seems to have broken it in his dream!"

The vet was an expert and chalked out a plan. He advised, "Prepare two hundred horses and line them up for action. Let the sound of guns and cannons thunder in the air. When these horses run, the limp horse will be shaken from its dream and gallop ahead."

It worked. The horse was awakened from its dream.

Just as the vision of the dream affected the horse, we, too, are influenced by the words of other people. They may confuse and mislead us from our faith in Bhagwan Swaminarayan. We feel our faith weaken but by constantly living within an atmosphere filled with words describing the glory of the Lord, we are awakened to the fact that Bhagwan Swaminarayan is the Supreme God.

WHO KILLED THE BRAHMINS?

There was once a *sheth*. He always generously gave alms. One day, four Brahmins arrived at his house. The *sheth* asked them to prepare a delicious lunch of *dudhpak*. While the Brahmins were making the *dudhpak* an eagle flew over them. The eagle was holding a snake. Unknown to the Brahmins, as the eagle flew over them, a drop of poison from the snake's mouth fell into the *dudhpak*. The Brahmins ate heartily but then immediately died.

Whose fault was it that the Brahmins died? The *sheth* was not to blame. Chitragupta, the chief judge of the god of death, Yama Raja, asked, "Yama Raja, on whose head shall I put the blame for this sin of killing four innocent Brahmins."

Even Yama Raja was puzzled. He said, "Let the matter wait a while. We'll decide later."

The next day, two more Brahmins came to the village. They asked an old lady the road to the generous *sheth's* house. Without bothering to seriously think, the old lady said, "He killed four yesterday and will kill two more today."

Yama Raja was watching all this. He immediately said, "Put the sin of killing the four Brahmins on this old lady's head."

The old lady wrongly accused the generous *sheth* and so she herself was given the sin of killing four Brahmins.

Never accuse anyone wrongly. Never comment on anything without first knowing the context.

'TAM SNANAM AM SNANAM!'

Two Brahmins took a vow to bathe in the river every morning for twelve months. There were no problems in the summer and monsoon months but things became difficult when winter arrived.

One day it was very cold. Snow had fallen. One Brahmin forced himself to get out of bed and went to the river. He thought to himself, "Let me first dip a finger in and see how cold the water is."

As soon as he dipped his finger in the river it froze numb.

The Brahmin wondered, "If this is what happens to my finger, then I'd die if I bathed in this water." He thought a while and then hit upon a plan. He picked up a pebble and throwing it into the water said, "*Kankaram snanam kalyanam krutam* – as the stone has bathed so have I!" He then began to return home satisfied and happy.

The second Brahmin was also coming to the river. He was surprised to see the first Brahmin returning so early. He asked, "How did you bathe in this cold?"

The first Brahmin explained, "I dipped this finger in the river and it became numb."

"Then how did you bathe?"

"I threw a pebble in and pretended I was the pebble!"

The second Brahmin at once touched the first Brahmin and said, *"Tam snanam am snanam* — In your bath I have had mine."* He also returned home!

Become a brave devotee. Never be a coward. Never fall back on a vow. One who safeguards a vow receives boundless merit.

FOUR FINGER FAITH

A man was digging a well. Even though he dug deep into the earth no water sprout forth. He soon lost patience. He stopped digging and climbed out of the well. Just near the well was a large piece of wood five hands long. One night a man was passing by. It was dark, and so he accidently kicked the wood. It hurt very much. He became angry. He was also very strong. He picked up the long piece of wood and threw it down into the well. The wood hit the ground so hard it dug four fingers deep into the ground and lo and behold, water sprouted forth. The wood had dug into an underground river. The well soon filled up and people from all around drank from it. The four inch curtain was broken.

Never lose patience. The final piece of earth – curtain – should be broken. Have patience while studying and listening to holy discourses. One who has patience attains his goals earlier.

A HUMBLE SERVANT OF GOD

Truly, King Ambarish was an humble servant of the Lord. He would serve Thakorji himself. For the Lord, he would collect fruits and flowers, make garlands, cook delicious food, wash the Lord's rich clothes — all by himself. Ambarish wouldn't even drink water without first offering it to God. He would offer everything to the Lord first and then only use it for himself.

For twenty hours a day he served the Lord in this manner. The king would take only four hours sleep. One day a thought struck him that four hours were being wasted in sleep. He began to serve the Lord for twenty-four hours.

The Lord appeared before him and said, "Ambarish, you are a king. You have a kingdom to rule. If you spend twenty-four hours in my service then when will you rule. And so it is my command, serve me for only three hours daily and use twenty-one hours to rule your kingdom." This is what King Ambarish then started to do.

Many say that when you associate with a holy Sadhu you disrupt your material life. But the Sadhu teaches both the road to a successful material life and the road to salvation. So all should come and associate.

TRICKING GOD

An old lady's son was ill. She prayed to God, "O God, if my son gets well I'll make you a *rotli* the size of the sky." Her son heard this and asked, "Mother, from where will you get a saucepan large enough to make a *rotli* as big as the sky?"

The old lady replied in a hushed voice, "Shh, son I'm tricking the Lord."

Never pray to the Lord in trickery. Pray with a true heart. God sees the hearts of all. He knows everything.

of gold have been stolen." His plan was to take home the remaining four chests.

The king realised the minister was deceiving him. Still he ordered, "Find the thieves." The minister thus tried for a month to find the thieves but couldn't do so. The king then proclaimed all over the kingdom, "He who has looted the king's treasure should present himself before the king at twelve o'clock." The king knew that the thief who had taken a vow always to tell the truth would come."

And the thief did come to the king at twelve' o'clock. He saluted the king and said, "Six of us thieves came to the palace and stole from the safe."

The king questioned him, "How many chests of gold did you take?"

"Sire, we took six chests."

The king said to his minister, " Minister, where are the other four chests?"

The minister said, "Sire, the thief is lying."

The king had been with the thieves when they had stolen the six chests of gold. He ordered his guards, "Go to the minister's house and search it."

The guards searched the house and found the four chests of gold. The minister couldn't say a word.

"Minister, you are the real thief. And this thief is truly honest." The king was very angry. He appointed the honest thief as the minister and jailed the old one.

All commands of the true Sadhu should be believed to hold total truth and so obeyed. One who does this attains Akshardham. Those who live a life of honesty and morality receive great rewards. Never be deceitful. If we harbour deceit like the minister, we will fall from the Lord's devotion and service.

BECOME A DOG

A Guru lived in the jungle. He stayed in a hut made of leaves. A dog went to live with the Guru, seeking his shelter. Whenever someone beat the dog it would tell the Guru. One day a man came into the forest. He beat the dog. The dog ran to the Guru and said, "Guru Maharaj, a man is beating me!"

The Guru said, "You become a man yourself!" In this way the Guru blessed the disciple dog and the dog was transformed into a man. The dog, now a man wandered into the jungle, not scared of the man who had beaten him.

One day, the dog, now a man, came across a tiger. The tiger attacked the dog-turned-man who at once ran to the Guru. He said to him, "A tiger attacked me!" The Guru blessed him, "Become a tiger yourself!" The man was transformed into a tiger. He now roamed the jungle at will.

One day the tiger was attacked by a lion. The tiger ran to the Guru. "A lion attacked me," he complained. The Guru replied, "Go, you yourself become a lion." He became a lion and was now scared of nobody.

And so it came to pass that one day a *sharabh* attacked the lion. The lion ran frightened to his Guru and said, "The *sharabh* attacked me." The Guru said, "Child, you yourself become a *sharabh*." He became a *sharabh* and fearlessly wandered the forest and began killing anyone he saw. He began to eat the people and animals he killed. Due to the Guru's blessing he became the most powerful beast in the whole jungle!

Once a thought came to him. "I have eaten all types of flesh. But I wonder what the Guru tastes like!" He forgot all about the Guru's blessings and grace. His mind became totally wicked and he decided to eat his Guru! The *sharabh* approached the Guru.

The Guru of course knew everything. He said to the *sharabh*, "You have achieved such power because of my blessings, and now you have come to eat me!" He cursed him, "Go, become a dog once again!" At once the *sharabh* became a dog. The Guru picked up a stick and chased him out of the *ashram*. And from then onwards wherever the dog went he was beaten.

It is God and His holy Sadhu who bless people with greatness. One should not then turn against them. The Guru may at any time say, "Go, become an ordinary person." Never at any time turn against the Guru or his disciples.

THE GREEDY PUJARI

There was once a Brahmin. He was a sincere devotee of God. Every *punam* he would walk to Dwarka and have *darshan* of Lord Ranchhodrai in the mandir.

One *punam*, a rich *sheth* gave the Brahmin a basketful of one hundred mangoes, saying he should offer the mangoes on his behalf to Lord Ranchhodrai in the mandir.

The road to Dwarka was long and hard, the Brahmin became tired and hungry and so, meditating on the Lord's *murti* in his mind, he ate a juicy ripe mango. One mango followed another. By the time he got to the mandir gates he had eaten ninety-nine mangoes. Only one remained in the basket!

The Brahmin placed the remaining mango before the *murti* of Lord Ranchhodrai, devoutly offered his prayers and began walking home. The *pujari* was greedy and was watching from behind a pillar. He took the mango into a corner and ate it quickly!

That night the Lord appeared in a dream to the *sheth* and said, "Of the one hundred mangoes you sent with my Brahmin devotee, I've received ninety-nine. One mango I haven't received!"

When the Brahmin returned home, the *sheth* called for him. He was quite upset. "Bhagat, the Lord appeared to me in a dream and said that he has received only ninety-nine mangoes. If you had only asked, I would have given you many mangoes. Good man, for only one mango you let your mind play with you. And now my desire to offer the Lord fully one hundred mangoes is incomplete."

The Brahmin was listening quietly all the while. When the *sheth* had finished his scolding, he said, "Sheth, to tell you the truth. I myself ate ninety-nine mangoes, and the mandir *pujari* ate the remaining one that I offered to the Lord."

The *sheth* was amazed. Then what of the Lord's words. He thought everything over. The truth slowly dawned on him. The Brahmin he had sent the mangoes with was a true devotee of Lord Ranchhodrai. So when the Brahmin had eaten the mangoes, he had mentally offered them to Lord Ranchhodrai first and then eaten them. The Lord accepted the mangoes though the Brahmin had eaten them. The one remaining mango was eaten by the mandir *pujari* in secret, without the slightest thought of the Lord. That mango did not reach the Lord!

One who serves a true Sadhu or devotee is really serving the Lord.

BUT WHY DID YOU SPEAK?

A prince in his previous birth had to suffer greatly because of his rude tongue. In this birth he remembered his unhappy last birth. And so from the moment he was born he wouldn't say a word!

One day in the garden a peacock began to sing. A hunter's attention was pulled to it and so he killed it. Seeing this, the prince unexpectedly said, "Why did the peacock speak!"

A guard heard these first words uttered by the prince. He at once went to the king with the good news, "The prince has spoken!" The king was overjoyed. He gave the guard a gift and distributed sanctified sugar crystals in court.

The king then began to play with the prince. But the prince wouldn't say anything. The king became angry, "The guard has played a trick on me! Have him killed by the cannon."

The guard was scared. He approached the prince and begged, "Prince, please speak just once to the king. Otherwise, he will have me killed by the cannon."

The prince said, "Why did you go and speak to the king in the first place? The peacock spoke and it died. You spoke and so you will die. And if I speak I will also die. So I'm not going to say anything."

The prince didn't utter a word more and so the king executed the guard.

Think before you speak. Never speak without good reason. Use speech sparingly, as one uses expensive ghee. Never speak spitefully of another.

There is absolutely no unhappiness in singing the praises of God and His holy Sadhu.

LINDIYO – THE LION-GOAT

Once, while out hunting, a lioness gave birth to a cub amid a flock of goats. She left her newly born baby amid the goats and returned to her den in the forest.

This baby lion began to live with the group of goats. He ate, slept and stayed with them. As he grew up, the shepherd named him Lindiyo, a name normally reserved for goats and sheep. The lion responded to his name, skipped and danced, like every tame animal. Lindiyo grew up into the full frame of a lion but he himself never knew it. To himself, he was only a weak, frail goat!

One day, while they were on lush pastures, a huge lion roared and attacked the flock. All the goats fled with fear; they ran in all directions to save their lives. Even Lindiyo scampered away. The lion was astounded and looked twice. "How did a lion get mixed up with a flock of goats?" he asked himself.

He leaped and chased Lindiyo and soon seized him. Lindiyo was trembling with fright. He shut his eyes tight.

"Hey, you!" the lion shook him, "You're a lion. How did you end up in this group of goats?"

"Please, let me go. My name is Lindiyo, sir, please let me go!" the lion-goat helplessly pleaded for mercy.

"Come, come! You're not a goat! Rather, goats are your daily dinner. Why have you lost your senses? Come with me to the riverside!"

So saying the lion dragged Lindiyo to the river bank and where the water was quite still, he showed him his own reflection.

"See, look at your face. It's like mine. You have a golden mane, see the paws and the claws, everything is like mine. You are a lion and not a goat."

He further taught him to stand tall and roar like a lion.

"Come on speak like I speak and roar; and remember these goats are our food, not friends."

Lindiyo suddenly realised his true identity and broke out from his shell of limitations. He himself roared and drove away the goats. He had become a lion from a lion-goat.

We too, suffer from a similar problem. Our true identity is *atma*, but we have somehow lost that knowledge and believe ourselves to be the body. We all see ourselves as Lindiyo. We must realise our real nature and identity as the *atma* and become the master of *maya* and not its slave. And to attain such knowledge, we need to approach the true Sadhu, who shows and convinces us that we are not Lindiyo but the pure and powerful *atma*.

KAKADHIRAJ

Some Garasiyos once held an assembly. Kakadhiraj and a swan happened to meet there. With Kakadhiraj – the leader of the crows – were a group of fifty other crows. The swan said to them, "I am superior to you." Kakadhiraj proposed a competition. He said, "Who can fly the fastest along that road?" The swan was a slow flyer, and so the crow sprinted ahead. They both returned to the assembly. Kakadhiraj was the first to get there. The other crows were pleased to see that Kakadhiraj was superior to the swan. The swan agreed and said, "Yes, you're superior."

After a while the swan proposed another competition. He said, "Come, let's fly over the sea." Kakadhiraj agreed and began to fly. He was ahead of the swan. But after a while some spray from the sea waves soaked the crow's wings and he fell into the sea. The swan felt sorry for him and plucked him up out of the sea. But Kakadhiraj flew to the crows and declared that he was superior. The swan was surprised. He thought, "Even though I saved him he boasts that he is superior."

The swan again proposed that they fly over the sea. Kakadhiraj agreed. He said, "I'll never be beaten." As soon as Kakadhiraj was over the sea he fell into it. The swan helped him out. But the proud crow said, "I can fly a hundred and one times more than this!" Although he had fallen into the sea he didn't admit defeat. Even the other fifty crows couldn't go farther than this. The crows couldn't be humble even in defeat.

Then the swan said, "Let's fly again." The crow jumped into the air, but his wings were wet from falling into the sea, so he only flew a short distance and then fell back into the sea. The swan let him flounder in the sea for a while. He then asked, "How far can you fly now?"

"As far as death, so please rescue me now!" Kakadhiraj begged. The swan lifted him up and the two returned to the assembly. The swan asked, "Who is superior? Kakadhiraj answered, "Swan are greater than crows. You have saved my life."

In the same way, those whose greatness stretches from eternity are truly great. All others fall short. The greatness of the true Sadhu is eternal.

THE ROBIN

Long ago a blind man and a lame were friends. The blind man was a great believer in omens. He could tell about good and bad omens. Once the friends were talking. The blind man said to the lame, "Brother, if a robin flys through the prongs of a plough three times, and if a person who sees him doesn't blink even the slightest while watching, it means that the omen is perfect. And then the watcher can raid any village he wants and nobody will ever be able to catch him."

One morning the lame was sitting by himself. He saw a chirping robin pass through the prongs of a plough. He watched it, careful not to blink his eyelids in the slightest. The robin passed through the prongs three times. The lame watched everything without blinking. "The omen for today is terrific," he said joyously.

The blind man asked, "What omen did you see?"

The lame said, "I saw a robin pass through the prongs of a plough three times."

The blind man asked, "But did your eyes blink while you were watching?"

"No, not at all," replied the lame.

"Then prepare at once," the blind man said. "We'll rob the bazaar in Vadodara in broad daylight. Sit on my shoulders and show me the road to

Vadodara." The lame climbed onto the blind man's shoulder. The blind man walked according to his directions. Between twelve and one in the afternoon they got to the gold bazaar in Vadodara. There the lame saw a large jewellery shop. The owner and his staff had forgotten to lock the safe before going to lunch. The other helpers in the shop were dozing.

There were many passersby. The lame said to the blind man, "The jewellery shop is open. The safe is open. And inside I can see yellow coins."

"That's the gold," said the blind man.

The lame asked, "There are many passersby. What shall we do?"

"Are you sure of the robin?" the blind man asked.

"Of that I'm sure, I saw it with my own eyes."

"You didn't blink did you?"

"No."

"Then why are you scared? Don't worry, just grab the loot."

And so the lame grabbed the gold coins from the safe.

He asked, "Shall I close the safe?"

The blind man said, "The owner can do that for himself! Lets get going and leave quickly."

With the lame and the gold coins on his back the blind man made off. Both made it safely out of the town. At about two-thirty the staff returned to the shop chewing *pan*. They saw that the safe was open and that the gold coins were no longer there. They were convinced that the shop had been raided.

They called the owner. Someone said that a blind man and a lame had been seen leaving the shop.

The owner called the police. They closed the main roads leading out of town. But by then the thieves were out of town.

Everyone in the town soon knew that a blind man and a lame had raided the jeweller in broad daylight. They were amazed. How could they have done it! Ten armed policeman on horseback went after the thieves.

At a short distance from the town the blind man and the lame were making their way along. The lame was always looking back. He saw the police on horseback. He became frightened and said, "Blind brother, the police are after us."

"Are you sure of the robin?" his friend asked.

"Brother, I saw it with my own eyes. There can be no change in that."

The blind man encouraged him, "Then no one can harm a hair on our heads. We just continue walking."

On one side of the road was a pile of hay. The thieves hid in it. The police passed them. After a while the blind man and the lame again took to the road. Later they took the path of a narrow lane, walking in a hollow. In the meantime, the police not finding the thieves had turned back. The lame saw them coming. He said to the blind man, "Blind brother, death is coming straight to us. The policemen are coming from the opposite direction."

The blind man asked again, "Are you sure of the robin?"

"There can be no change in that," said the lame.

"Then let the police do what they can. Nothing is going to happen to us."

The police saw the two. They decided to ambush the thieves. So five policemen hid on each side of the lane, with their guns ready. They fired their guns. But the lame man ducked. And so the bullets hit the policemen on the other side, with the result that all ten policemen died! Only the horses returned to the town.

The blind man and the lame returned to their homes safely. The omen proved true.

The robin's passing through the prongs of a plough three times is of significance in three ways: (1) Sahajanand Swami is the Lord of all incarnations and is Purna Purushottam Narayan – God Supreme; (2) Gunatitanand Swami is Mul Aksharbrahma; and (3) Satpurush, the true Sadhu, is our gateway to liberation. These three principles should be a bedrock in our lives.

The moral behind the lame man not blinking is that we should never see the actions of the Satpurush as human. If this is firmly affixed in our devotion, then we will never need to be afraid of *kal,* karma, and *maya* just as the blind man and the lame were not scared of being caught or dying. If these beliefs are not deeply rooted in our hearts then even God cannot help us.

GREATNESS OF SATSANG

Naradji once went to Shri Krishna. He asked, "What are the fruits of doing *satsang*?" "Naradji," said the Lord pointing to a big worm, "This worm in hell will explain to you the benefits of doing *satsang*."

So Naradji went to the worm in hell and asked, "Worm, what are the fruits of doing *satsang*?" The worm looked at Naradji and then died! Naradji didn't get an answer. So he returned to the Lord and said, "I didn't get an answer to my question, and the worm died. Now you must give me an answer."

The Lord heard Naradji but said, "Look, see that nest, in it is a newly born parrot. Go and ask it. The baby parrot will explain to you the fruits of doing *satsang*."

With this command from God, Naradji approached the little baby parrot and asked, "What are the fruits of *satsang*?" The baby parrot opened its eyes and looked at Naradji. But then died! This frightened Naradji. He began to think, "The benefit of *satsang* is death! Whoever I ask this question to dies."

He made his way to the Lord. With great unhappiness he said, "If you want to tell me the truth then please tell me. Because whoever I ask dies. Murder hangs on my head now. I don't think I can take your advice again."

The Lord laughed at this. He said, "Naradji, don't be upset. If you really want an answer to your question then go and ask that newly-born calf." Still sad with the death of the baby parrot, Narad approached the newborn calf and softly asked in its ear, "What are the fruits of *satsang*?" Naradji stood still waiting for an answer. The calf looked at Naradji and toppled to the ground. It died. Naradji was now extremely depressed. He had now sinned by killing a cow. He quickly went to the Lord to speak his mind. He was going to tell him off! But the Lord calmed him down and said, "You will certainly get the answer to your question now. The king has a newborn boy. Go ask the baby prince your question."

Naradji said to the Lord, "Upto now I've asked a worm, a parrot, and a calf, and they've all died. I've been lucky that nobody has troubled me so far. But if the king's son dies then I'll be in deep trouble. So now I don't want to know the fruits of doing *satsang*!" The Lord assured Naradji that the prince would definitely explain to him the benefits of doing *satsang* and he would not die.

Naradji, with a brave heart, went to the palace and asked the prince, "Brother, what are the fruits of *satsang*?" Hearing this the prince looked at Naradji, and laughed. He answered, "Naradji, haven't you understood the greatness of *satsang* yet? When you first asked me the question I was a worm. I then died and became a parrot. But with your *darshan* at my nest I died and was given the body of a calf. Then again with your *darshan* I was freed and given this highest of births, as a human being. And now with the grace of your *darshan* I have been fulfilled. If just by your *darshan* I have gained so much then think how much a person can gain by associating *(satsang)* with a great sadhu such as yourself!" Naradji now fully understood the greatness of *satsang*. He returned to the Lord and praised, "Lord, your divine ways will never be understood by anyone."

MONEY! MONEY!

Four friends were performing austerities in the forest to gain money. Everyday they chanted "Money, Money!" Once, a voice called from the skies saying, "Friends, you will find a lot of money, but at the same time it will bring a lot of misery."

"Let it be so," the four said. "Let all the miseries of the universe fall upon us, but let wealth be ours."

Suddenly, a solid cube of gold fell from the heavens. All four of them danced with joy. Then, as time went by, each began to think.

"How good it would be if I alone owned the gold."

And so, they paired in twos. And both pairs devised plans to kill the other. One pair told the other, "Today, let us celebrate for the gold we have found. Let's eat a superb feast of *ladus*. So you two go to town and buy *ladus* while the two of us guard the gold."

"Agreed." So saying the other two left.

The remaining two schemed. "When they return we shall ask them to fetch water from the well and push them in. And finally stone them to death."

The two in town planned, "Let us poison the *ladus* and let them eat themselves to death." They made the poisonous *ladus*, sumptuous, well greased with ghee and made simple ones for themselves. On returning, they left the *ladus* at the place where they were to celebrate by having a picnic and went to fetch water as asked. The other two pushed them in and murdered them.

After the evil deed was done, the remaining two returned to eat. Looking at the *ladus* they cursed, "Those two crooks! They made sumptuous *ladus* oozing with ghee for themselves and simple ones for us. Let's enjoy the best and forget the rest."

So saying they ate the poisonous *ladus* and met their death.

Two died in the well, and two died outside the well. The gold remained unclaimed on the road.

It is said in the Shrimad Bhagvat, "Gold is the home of evil." This is true. Gold makes brothers bite and fight. So never lust after wealth.

'TWO I HAVE DONE, YOU DO ONE!'

There was a guru who was very peaceful and very knowledgeable. He spent his time singing the glory of God.

Once, along with his disciple he arrived at a village. It was a rainy day and they had become exhausted. Night fell. And they prepared to sleep in a small mandir. Both of them lay on the floor, but the lamp had been left burning. The guru asked the disciple, "It is time to sleep, so snuff out the lamp!"

The disciple quipped, "Oh just cover your head with your blanket. It will be as good as putting out the lamp."

Then, after a while, the guru asked, "Please see if it is still raining outside or not." Just then a cat entered through the mandir door. It had come from outside. The disciple said, "Just stroke the cat with your hand. If it is wet then you'll know that it is still raining."

Next, the guru commanded, "We must sleep now, so go and close the main door."

"But two jobs I have done, now you do one," the disciple complained.

Such disciples never progress on the spiritual path. The real disciple should obey each and every command of his guru. Only by implicit obedience does he attain the divine virtues of his guru. Never answer back or be cheeky towards your guru. Only then will you rise in the spiritual world.

THE CALF TRIES TO SUCKLE THE BULL

One day a calf got lost from its mother and wandered away to the cowshed. "Let me drink some fresh milk," it said to itself. It skipped and danced in delight and approached the first animal in the shed. It was a bull.

Every time the calf thrust its head under the bull's belly, the bull violently kicked it. Foolishly, the calf continued to try for milk, and it kept on getting kicked; so much so that its mouth and face became swollen. And when in the end it returned to its rightful mother, its mouth was too bruised and bashed to be able to suck milk. It could not even suck at its mother's udders.

On the spiritual path, when one strays away from the enlightened Sadhu and pokes one's head elsewhere to gain happiness from others, it is like receiving kicks one after the other. By approaching and associating with people of lower calibre we damage our faith and conviction in God and are lost in a world of misunderstandings.

A MILLION RUPEE DIAMOND

On the road from Junagadh to Vanthali, there is a deep stepwell called Khengar Vav. Near the stepwell there once lived a poor, blind man. He always cried and begged to the travellers passing by, "O kind people. Give me something to eat. I've been starving for the last two days. Please have mercy on this poor man."

He had one close friend who was a woodcutter. Daily the woodcutter would sit half-an-hour with him and offer some snacks. Nobody else really spoke to the poor man.

But one day, it so happened that a wealthy *sheth* was journeying along in a horse carriage. He had a generous heart and gave charity to everyone. On seeing the poor or the hungry, he would slip his hand into his coat pocket and gave away the first thing that came into his hand. The *sheth* felt compassion for the blind beggar and instantly put his hand into his pocket. And lo and behold. It was a million rupee diamond that his hand picked out. "The poor man seems to have fortunate stars today," thought the *sheth*. He went closer to the blind man and placed the diamond in his grubby hand saying, "Blind man, you have struck good fortune. I'm giving you a million rupee diamond." No sooner had he grasped the diamond within his palm, the blind man forgot his hunger, his poverty and his pain. A light of peace and delight shone upon his face. The *sheth* explained further, "Take this diamond to the market in Junagadh. It will bring you a million rupees. Buy a bungalow from it, hire a cook, keep a servant, and invest the money. Your whole life you shall now be able to pass in peaceful happiness." Then the *sheth* left.

Evening fell. The pauper's friend, the woodcutter, had returned after his daily selling of wood. Seeing the blind man's face bubbling with joy he inquired, "What makes you so happy today?"

The blind man enthusiastically narrated the whole event and showed him the diamond. It was sparkling from all sides.

"Never! The *sheth* would never give away a diamond," the woodcutter snapped. "It seems that he has given you a crystal of poison."

He cast a huge cloud of suspicion across the blind man's mind. The woodcutter had brought fresh jaggery for his friend to eat. Taking it out he said, "Here, taste this. If this cheap, two paise worth of jaggery tastes so sweet, then just imagine how sweet a million rupee diamond should taste!" He gave him some jaggery to eat. It tasted sweet! Then he asked him to lick the diamond. It was horribly bitter.

The poor man's naive mind confirmed his doubt. "So where shall I throw this crystal?"

"Not on the road because even if some stray cow or dog eats it, it will die. And if a passerby picks it up, he too will die. Throw it in this deep stepwell. It should be safe in there. No one will be harmed by it."

The blind man had only to let it drop and it sank – all the way to the bottom. And he, too, sank into his original depression and sat on the edge of the stepwell to begin his routine of begging.

Sometime later, the *sheth* returned along the path. He was shocked at seeing the blind man in the same poor condition. He inquired about the diamond, but the blind man swore at him and abused him for trying to poison him; he spoke about the sweetness of jaggery, how he cast away the bitter crystal... The *sheth* learnt of the man's foolery and went away disappointed. He returned with a workforce of labourers who worked day and night to empty the stepwell. Villagers from the nearby villages were surprised as to why the *sheth* was spending so much money to empty the stepwell. They kept guessing at the amount it would cost and the *sheth* firmly continued his task. After weeks of day and night work, the water level was lowered. The divers were sent to the bottom to bring out the top layer of the mud. Whole bucketfuls were piled on the edge. The mud was searched painstakingly. After three more days the diamond was found. Putting it back in his pocket, the *sheth* left without a further word.

The moral of the story is that this human birth that we have is as rare and precious as a diamond. But our friends advise us to discard it. They tempt us away from Satsang and the holy atmosphere. Do not waste this life. God has gifted it to us, so make the most of it.

THE ILLUSIONIST

There was once an illusionist. He would show his tricks to kings and win prizes from them. One day the illusionist went before a king, taking along his wife and sons. He said to the king, "There is a war in heaven. I have to go there immediately and help call a truce between the gods and demons. Kindly look after my wife and children while I'm away."

The king agreed. The illusionist then unwound a bundle of rope he had with him and raised it into the air. A miracle. The rope climbed higher and higher, remaining straight and taut all the while.

The illusionist climbed the rope and disappeared into the sky. The king and his ministers saw all this.

After about an hour, gunshots and cannon-fire could be heard in the sky. Everybody could hear the booms and thunders. Another half-hour passed in this way.

And then... all of a sudden, two hands fell out of the sky and dropped at the king's feet. Incredibly, they were the illusionist's hands! And then his legs fell too, followed by his body, but without his head. The illusionist's wife recognised the illusionist and began to wail. In between sobs she told the distressed and confused king, "Bring some logs. I'm a faithful wife, and I will die with my husband on his funeral pyre!" Even the illusionist's children said they would die in the fire!

The logs were brought. The hands, feet and headless body of the illusionist were placed on the pyre. The fire was lighted, and the faithful wife and her children climbed onto the pyre and began to burn with the wood!

As the assembly watched the fire, the illusionist climbed down the rope, as whole and alive as ever! "Where are my wife and children," he demanded. The king and his people really were confused now. If this was the illusionist, then who was burning in the fire?

The king plucked up courage and said to the illusionist, "Your wife and children are burning in the fire over there."

"No, they're not," said the illusionist. "You've hidden them somewhere and now you're lying to me. Bring them here at once!" No one could say a word. The illusionist again said angrily, "If you don't call my wife and children, I will!"

Before anybody could say anything in reply, he shouted, "Hey kids, where are you!" And his kids shouted in reply from the third floor of the palace! "See they are here. You've hidden them on the third floor."

The king really was flabbergasted. "You bring them here then," he commanded the illusionist.

"Then give me the keys."

"I don't have them!"

"Yes, you do, they're under your throne!"

The bewildered king looked and sure enough the keys to his palace were there. The third floor was duly opened and the illusionist's wife and children were brought downstairs. The king and his ministers couldn't believe their eyes. Had they all gone mad? The illusionist and his family were supposed to be dead and burning, but here they were, alive and well.

"How did you do it," the king asked the illusionist of his illusion.

"Oh, it's just a little game I play everyday," the illusionist said proudly. His family was used to all of his tricks. They weren't worried or confused in the least. The children told the king, "Daddy plays such tricks on people everyday."

Nobody has been able to work out how the illusionist performed his tricks. If an illusionist's illusion can never be understood, how can we ever hope to understand the workings of God! It is only when we become a devotee of God that we are not taken in and misguided by the illusory world around us.

THE UNITY OF THE DOVES

Once a flight of doves spotted some grains and landed on them to eat. They were quietly enjoying their meal, when suddenly a birdcatcher threw a net over them. Just then, the 'supervisor' dove, the leader, advised, "If each one of us attempts to fly in his own way, this net will be impossible to lift. Let us all become one and rise together."

They all united their efforts and flew away with the net. Up ahead, they settled onto a tree and slowly escaped from beneath while the net hung over the branches.

If we remember this unity of the doves as an example and unite our efforts, then Bhagwan Swaminarayan will be pleased upon us and fountains of joy will spring from within. So long as we remain one and are backed by the strength of God nothing can harm us.

MOTHER MONKEY STANDS ON HER BABY

Mother monkey, with her baby clinging to her chest was crossing a river. Suddenly, the water level began to rise. Indeed, the love of a mother for her baby is great. And so, the monkey placed her little one on her shoulders. The water was now chest high, and was rapidly rising higher. To save her offspring from drowning, the monkey picked it up and perched it safely on her head. She had no choice but to wait and allow the water's flow to lessen. Instead, the rise continued and now she stood neck deep. Within a few moments the water level climbed upto her nose. She saw her own death approaching. Instinctively she threw her baby into the water and stepped on it to climb a few inches higher.

See how attached one is to one's body? To save herself the mother climbed upon her own baby. Just as we love our body more than we love our friends and family, we should cultivate greater love for God and His holy Sadhu – like the love we have for our body.

ARUNI AND UPMANYU

Once, there were two disciples of Rishi Ayuddhoumya. Their names were Aruni and Upmanyu. Both were young and very quiet. They obeyed the Guru in everything. Once the Guru decided to test them to the full. He sent them to the forest to graze the ashram's cows. He also ordered them, "Don't eat anything." Both disciples always obeyed the Guru, and so they ate nothing. But whenever they felt hungry they would milk a cow and drink some milk.

After some days the Guru asked, "What do you eat?" They replied, "We eat nothing cooked but do drink milk." The Guru said, "From now on, don't drink milk either." The disciples agreed and went happily off to the forest to graze the cows. In the afternoon both felt hungry, but the Guru had ordered them not to drink even milk now. And so they went to a village and begged pieces of fruit and ate them. Thus they began to do this everyday.

A few days later, the Guru asked "What do you eat?" They replied, "We beg pieces of fruit from the village and eat those." The Guru instructed, "We should never beg in this way." So the two promised never to beg again.

Aruni and Upmanyu again went to the forest to graze the cows. Never did they find fault with their Guru. For three to four days they managed to survive without food. But hunger grew and they could bear it no longer. The

Guru had commanded not to eat or drink milk. So they ate some wild berries. The berries were poisonous and the two became blind. As they made their way back to the ashram holding each other's hand they fell into a dry well one hundred hands deep.

Seeing the cows return alone to the ashram the Guru became worried. Where were Aruni and Upmanyu? He set out in search of them.

He searched the jungle calling, "Hey Aruni, Hey Upmanyu." He couldn't see them anywhere. However, the two disciples heard their Guru calling and shouted a reply from the bottom of the well. "Where are you?" the Guru shouted.

"Over here, in the well," they called back.

The Guru had some people climb down into the well and bring the two disciples up. When he saw them he realised they had become blind! He asked the reason for this. They humbly answered, "You commanded us not to eat or drink anything, but we were so hungry that we ate some wild berries. They were poisonous and then we became blind. And as we tried to make our way back to the ashram, we fell into this empty well."

The rishi was extremely pleased with their devotion to him. He called Ashwinikumar, the physician of the gods. He gave them potent medicine and so both boys could see again.

The Guru so tested his young disciples, but they were not discouraged. They did not run away and leave the Guru. It is because of this that the Guru was pleased with them.

Nowadays are we tested in this way? No!

We should be quiet and meek. Never pamper the body. Involve the body rigorously in spiritual discourses and service.

We should, with enthusiasm and ardour, strive to please our Guru and God.

EVIL MONEY

An aspirant once took some money to a true Sadhu. He was well-intentioned and wanted to donate it. But the money was evil. It had previously been stolen.

The disciple asked, "What shall we do with the money?"

Of course, the true Sadhu knew all about the money, so he answered, "If you keep this money, or if I keep it, or if we give it to somebody else, wherever it will go it will destroy the life of the keeper. Even if some food is bought with it, the eater's mind will be disturbed. There is only one answer. Throw the money into the holy Ganga as the Lord has bathed in her waters. By doing this, the owner of the money will find salvation."

The disciple was faithful. "Whatever you say," he said, and threw the evil money into the Ganga.

Wrongly begotten wealth destroys the unrightful owner.

HORSE-RIDING FROM A BOOK

One young man went to a library in Mumbai. He picked up a book titled "How to Ride a Horse" and read it. He studied the skills of how to mount a horse, how to put the foot in the stirrup, how to hold the reins and many other things. Then, one day, he went as a guest to the house of a Darbar. There was a healthy-looking horse there. On seeing it, he could not contain himself from bragging, "I've learnt how to ride a horse, so let me ride this horse."

"Alright, go on," consented the Darbar.

He attempted to climb the horse. But a horse always recognises a rider. The Darbar's horse realised that here was a stranger and beginner. It reared up and flung the young man to the ground. The Darbar asked, "Where did you learn to ride?"

"I learnt from a book in the Mumbai library," he said, exposing his foolishness.

One must remember that one cannot learn anything by oneself, one needs a teacher, a Guru, in everything one does.

DESHAL AND ZAKHARO

Deshal Darbar and Zakharo Charan were two good friends. They were so close that at times they even wore each other's clothes. They were inseparable.

They lived together under one roof and never saw fault with one another.

In the same village lived another Darbar. He envied the two friends because of their friendship and decided to make friends with Zakharo. So one fine day he said, "Zakharo, why don't you come and stay with me!"

Zakharo was ready and replied, "Coming just now!"

The two new friends lived happily together. One day the Darbar had a delicious feast prepared and affectionately served Zakharo. The two then went to the river for a swim. Zakharo came out of the water early and immediately put on the Darbar's clothes!

When the Darbar came out of the water and saw Zakharo wearing his clothes, he said, "Why, Zakharobhai! How come you have worn my clothes?"

Zakharo the Charan sang:

"What clothes have we worn,

What clothes will we wear yet;

On this body of ours,

This is mine and this is yours, never spoke Deshal."

Zakharo quickly took off the Darbar's clothes and put on his own. He straight away left the Darbar and returned to his friend Deshal.

The oneness between God and His true Sadhu is like that of Deshal and Zakharo. There are never two voices or opinions. They are always and forever one.

Such oneness between friends prevents *maya* from disturbing their devotion.

GLOSSARY

As with all languages, many Gujarati words have no English equivalent. Other words when translated convey only a partial meaning. A literal translation of these words would have taken away all sparkle and freshness from *101 Tales of Wisdom*. Therefore, many such key words have been kept in the original Gujarati with only a transliteration given in the text. Explanations and meanings are given in this glossary.

A

adu	the side panel of a oxen cart
Akshardham	the divine abode of Bhagwan Swaminarayan
Ambarish	a very devoted Hindu king
antahkaran	inner seat of thought and feeling
ashram	a place where a guru stays with his disciples
atma	soul
atmanivedi	one who has totally surrendered to God

B

Baniya	a businessmen community. Also called Vaniya
barfi	a sweet delicacy

bhagat	a pious person
Bhaktachintamani	a scripture about Bhagwan Swaminarayan written in verse by Nishkulanand Swami
Bhal	a region of Gujarat
bhajan	devotional lyrics
bhavaiya	a minstrel who tours the countryside
Bhudev	a colloquial term for a Brahmin
brahmachari	a celibate
Brahmin	one of the four major divisions of Hindu society. Traditionally it is the Brahmins who perform the many rites and ceremonies for mandirs and families

C

Charan	a bard
charan	holy feet
Chitragupta	assistant to Lord Yama, the god of death, who presides over hell
chorashi	an occasion in which Brahmins are given a special meal and gifts

D

Darbar	of the warrior class
darbar	the the house or court of the leader Darbar.

yug false sadhus can be compared to black *hansa*. Those who encourage devotion and live a disciplined life in keeping with *dharma-niyams* are true *hansa*. With just a word they cleanly separate the truth from falsity, worldly pleasures from spiritual joy. One who can destroy our worldly desires and attachment is a true *hansa* – true Sadhu

Hutashani	the festival of colours. Also known as Fuldol and Holi

I

indriya	sense organ, eg. eye, ear, nose

J

jai	call of victory
Janak	historic king famous for his piousness and devotion

K

Kachiya	a community
Kali-yug	the period of time from the birth of the universe to its ultimate destruction is divided into four spans or yugs. These are, in order, Satya-yug, Dwapar-yug, Treta-yug and Kali-yug.

The people who live in Satya-yuga live much longer and are very noble and virtuous. Progressively through the remaining three time periods, people become evil, losing their nobleness and virtues, not worshipping God. The end of Kali-yug is said to be the most evil time in the history of the universe. In the vast time span of these four periods, our universe has only just entered Kali-yug.

Kartik	the twelveth month of the Hindu calendar.
Kashi	a holy city on the banks of the Ganga famous as a centre of learning and pilgrimage. It is also known as Varanasi and Benares
khir	a hot, thick sweet delicacy from milk, sugar, rice and dry fruits. Is similar to *dudhpak*.
kirtan	devotional song
Koli	A community

L

ladu	A sweet delicacy in the form of a ball. Is said to be much loved by Brahmins

M

mahatma	A great soul

Maharashtra	A state in India
mantra (1)	a sacred word or sentence, which when continually repeated with devotion gives great spiritual benefit.
mantra (2)	a chant used in magic and witchcraft
Marwad	a district of Rajasthan state
maund	unit of weight. 1 *maund* equals 20 kilogrammess
maya	Ignorance
mesub	a sweet delicacy – regarded as the king of sweets
Mt. Girnar	famous pilgrimage mountain just outside Junagadh
muhurt	special times of the day during which special ceremonies are to be performed. Thus, a marriage ceremony, the opening of a new store or laying the foundation stone of a mandir will not be performed at a randomly chosen date or time, but carefully fixed after first consulting the appropriate astrological texts. Is often pronounced 'murat'.
murti	sacred idol of God that is revered and worshipped.

N

nadu	a string that is tightened around the waist to hold up the traditional pyjama-type trousers.
Narad	an ancient sage of India known to be very close to God

niyam	moral and spiritual disciplines, and religious codes of conduct prescribed by God, the Satpurush, or the scriptures. Bhagwan Swaminarayan has outlined the basic niyams for all of His followers in the Shikshapatri

P

Pahi mam	"save me!"
paramhansas	'supreme swan'. A male sadhu of the highest order, characterised by his ability to discriminate between *sat* and *asat* – just as swans were traditionally considered to be able to distinguish between milk mixed with water.
Param Ekantik	a devotee of the highest spiritual state
parshad	a person who becomes a sadhu in the Swaminarayan Sampraday passes through two initiations. The first is *parshad*, wherein he wears white robes, but observes the full vows of a sadhu. The second initiation is that of a sadhu, who wears ochre robes
pujari	the priest of a mandir who performs the necessary rites and rituals
punyadan	donation worthy of merit
Puran	ancient Hindu scriptures

puri	small, flat and round fried pieces of wheat dough. Usually eaten with curried vegetables.

R

rayan	a berry-like, slightly sweet fruit that grows on the rayan tree
Ranchhodrai	another name for Lord Krishna
rotli	thin, soft, circular bread of wheat flour
rotlo	thick coarse bread made of millet flour, usually the staple diet of villagers

S

sadhu	a person who renounces the world to concentrate all his energies on worshipping God and serving society. He lives a life of celibacy and poverty, the degree of which varies from order to order.
samadhi	trance
sher	a unit of weight – approximately one half of a kilo-gramme
shak	cooked spiced vegetables
Sanjeevani	a medicine that brings the dead back to life
Sankhya	a system of philosophy, teaching that the world and everything in it is temporary. Only God is permanent

	– eternal.
Sanskrit	the ancient language of India, often referred to as the 'mother of languages'.
Satsang	*sat* = truth or good, *sang* = company or group. *Satsang* refers to keeping the company of pious and virtuous people. Satsang is also used to describe the entire Swaminarayan Sampraday
Sharad Purnima	15th day of the bright half of Aso (Oct-Nov). The birthday of Gunatitanand Swami
sharabh	a legendary predatory wild animal
shastri	a person learned in Sanskrit texts and scriptures
sheth	a rich merchant or businessman
Shikshapatri	a small scripture of 212 two-line verses written by Bhagwan Swaminarayan. It outlines the moral and spiritual rules and regulations of life to be obeyed by all His followers.
shethani	wife of a *sheth*
Shivji	Lord Shiv, responsible for the destruction of the world at the end of time
Shivling	the symbol of Lord Shiv that is worshipped
shuli	a traditional method of execution wherein the convicted is laid flat on wooden boards and an iron stake is driven through his body

sud	the bright half of a month. So Kartik *sud* means 'the bright half of the month of Kartik.'
Sudarshan Chakra	a small disc-like revolving weapon used by Lord Krishna
Swamini Vato	practical teachings of Gunatitanand Swami based on the Vacahnamrut. Penned first-hand by his leading sadhus disciples.

T

tal	sesame seed
tapasvi	a person who performs *tap* – austerities
Thakorji	the small metal *murtis* of the Lord found in homes and mandirs
Trahi toba	"Save me! I'm done for!"
Treta-yug	the second of the four yugs (see Kali-yug)
tumbdi	gourd
tulsi	a shrub with small green leaves regarded as especially holy by Hindus

V

Vachanamrut	teachings of Bhagwan Swaminarayan compiled in His own lifetime and authenticated by Him. The primary scripture of the Swaminarayan Sampraday.

vad	the dark half of a month. So Kartik *vad* means 'the dark half of the month of Kartik'.
Videhi	one who is not attached to his body
Vaikunth	the divine abode of Bhagwan Ram

Y

Yogeshwars	there were nine great ascetic brothers known as the 'Nine Yogeshwars'.

PRESENT from NAINA & KIRTESH TALSANIA
(SAT) 20 JUNE 2009 @ #16 ST MARY'S